CAPITAL CITY PARAMEDIC

Second edition
published in 2006 by

WOODFIELD PUBLISHING
Woodfield House, Babsham Lane, Bognor Regis
West Sussex PO21 5EL, England.

Capital City
Paramedic

THE LIFE & TIMES OF A
LONDON AMBULANCEMAN

JOHN KINSLEY

Woodfield

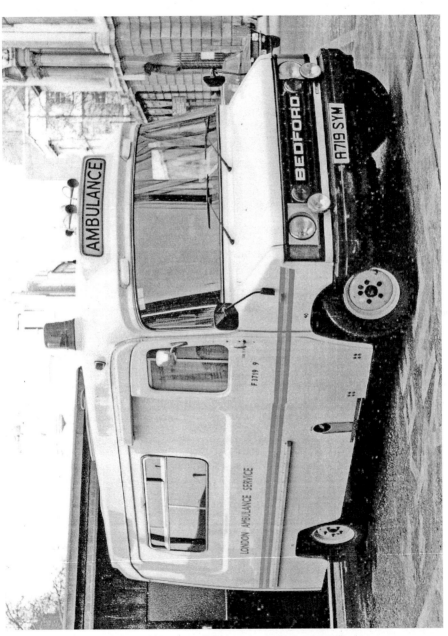

*Bedford ambulance of the type in service in the 1970s at
Smithfield Ambulance Station in the City of London.*

Contents

Preface 7

The London Ambulance Service 9

Glossary of terms... 11

Acknowledgements.. 13

Prologue.. 15

Part I   Selection.. 19

Part II   Training.. 25

Part III   Bloomsbury A&E Training Station 55

Part IV   New Malden, Tolworth and Richmond 127

Part V   Streatham , The Oval & Paramedic Training 165

Part VI   The Island 201

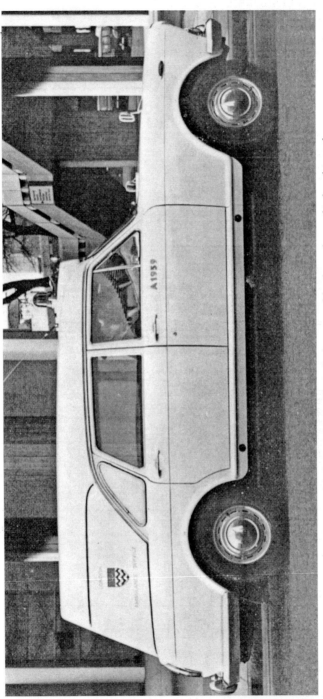

Limousine-type ambulance – 1970s. This vehicle was used by the author on his last day at the training station for a round trip from London to South Wales. (see page 122)

Preface

Capital City Paramedic is the true story of ambulanceman John E. Kinsley who served with the London Ambulance Service from March 1975 until September 1982. The book follows his progress from selection and induction at the Waterloo headquarters of the LAS, on-road training at the hectic Bloomsbury accident and emergency ambulance station in Central London and through his work as a Leading Ambulanceman and Paramedic at several South London ambulance stations in the years to follow.

The huge area of operations covered by the London ambulance service, ensured that, in the course of his career, John attended just about every kind of emergency situation, including some extraordinary ones, including IRA terrorist attacks, the Brixton riots and the London visit of his holiness the Pope...

The stories are based on actual events, although some dates, names of patients, police officers, hospital medical staff and ambulance personnel have been changed, for obvious reasons.

A London Ambulance of the 1970s, seen here leaving Waterloo Accident and Emergency Ambulance Training Station.

The London Ambulance Service

The London Ambulance Service came into being on
1st April 1965 and combines the services previously operated
in the 620 square miles of the Greater London area by the
County Councils of London, Middlesex, Surrey, Kent, Essex
and Hertfordshire, and also the County Borough Councils
of East Ham, West Ham and Croydon. It has a fleet of a
thousand vehicles based at 76 stations. Two thousand five
hundred operational and control staff serve the needs of
over eight million people and about four hundred hospitals,
clinics, etc.

Over three million patient journeys are made annually,
and the total distance run in a year exceeds fifteen million
miles. For operational management purposes the service is
divided into four divisions. Each division is controlled by a
Divisional Ambulance Officer and sub-divided into areas
under the direction of Area Superintendents. Ambulance
stations fall into two categories, large main stations with
several vehicles and small 'satellite' stations with just one or
two ambulances each. Each main station operates under the
control of a station superintendent, who is also responsible
for one, two or sometimes three satellite stations.

The control organisation of the service consists of six
ambulance controls as follows: North West at Kenton, North

East at Ilford, South West at New Malden and South East at Bromley. The Central Hospital Zone control is based alongside the Central Emergency Control at the service Headquarters at Waterloo. The Chief Control Superintendent is responsible to the Chief Ambulance Officer for the control organisation.

An important feature of the organisation of the Service is the initial training of the new entrants and the provision of refresher training for established ambulance personnel. This is carried out through the Training Officers, again based at the training school at service Headquarters.

Advanced training (Paramedic) is also carried out at the Waterloo training school and at several London Hospitals, under the supervision of casualty, operating-theatre and anaesthetic staff, followed by examinations carried out by doctors attached to LAS Headquarters.

N.B. The above introductory information is based on the LAS as it was during the years 1973 – 1982 when the author was a serving London Ambulanceman.

Glossary of Terms

PURPLE ANNEX .... Hospital mortuary.

B.B.A. .... Baby born before arrival.

B.I.D. .... Bought in dead.

BLUE .... Ambulance mobile with priority case.

BROWN .... Ambulance mobile with non-urgent case

D.I.C. .... Died in hospital casualty department

D.O.A. .... Dead on arrival

GREEN .... Ambulance available for a call

INDIA .... Ambulanceman / woman trained in
advanced resuscition procedures

PURPLE .... Patient with no visible life signs

PURPLE PLUS .... Patient beyond medical aid

RED .... Accident / emergency call

RED BASE .... Emergency control room

R/T .... Radio telephone.

R.T.A. .... Road traffic accident

R.T.B. .... Return to base station

WHITE .... non – urgent call

A difficult patient removal at London Docks during ambulance training.

Acknowledgements

My thanks go to the Chief Ambulance Officer of the London Ambulance Service for his kind permission to use material and photographs obtained from the archives stored in the service museum at Ilford. Also to 'Mr Personality', Terry Spur MBE – who founded the LAS museum – for his time and help in providing me with the information required for me to get this book on the right path. Once again, many, many thanks.

John Kinsley

London Ambulancemen practice a difficult removal during training.

Prologue

Nearly everyone in the developed world will at some time in their life be transported as a patient on board an ambulance: perhaps as an accident victim, after a sudden illness or on their way to hospital from home at the request of their doctor. It is can be a frightening experience, due to the fear of pain and the unknown.

My turn to be transported as a patient came out of the blue at the end of November 1998 when my wife called for an ambulance through the 999 system after I had collapsed at home with chest pains…

Within a short time the ambulance crew arrived, made their assessment and with reassurances, removed me to the ambulance where I was placed, sitting upright, on the trolley-bed. With oxygen administered and further blood pressure readings taken, we started the journey towards St Mary's hospital at Newport on the Isle-of-Wight. It felt strange to be 'on the other side of the fence', so to speak, after many years of treating and transporting all types of patients as an ambulanceman myself and later as a paramedic with the London Ambulance Service.

On arrival at St Mary's hospital, full of apprehension, I was wheeled into the Coronary Care Unit. My turn had come to be treated. After moving me across to a hospital bed from the ambulance trolley the crew made their departure wishing me all best.

The next couple of hours were taken up with doctors coming and going, drips and drugs being administered, monitor leads being attached to various parts of my anatomy, blood tests, pressure readings and questions being asked relating to my work and way of life. Eventually, my wife was allowed into the unit to see me.

"How do you feel now?" she asked, leaning forward and kissing me on the cheek.

"A lot better than a few hours ago," I replied, with a little smile.

"The sister has asked me to say goodnight to you, because they want you to rest at the moment, so I'm going to get a taxi home and I'll see you early tomorrow afternoon," she said, kissing me again and squeezing my hand. With tears in her eyes, she turned, waved and headed for the double doors and the exit.

"Who's been a lucky boy then!" the sister said, raising my hand to take my pulse yet again.

"I heard from the ambulance crew that brought you in and from your wife, that you used to be in the service as a paramedic – is that right?"

"Yes – a few years ago in London," I replied.

"So you have an idea what has happened to you?" she said placing my hand back on the bed.

"Heart attack – yeah?" I said, raising my eyes.

"Yes. It looks like you have had an MI. The doctors will be making more tests in the morning – but for now I want you to rest. Try to get some sleep and I will see you later."

She smiled before turning away to attend to the patient in the opposite bed.

I was alone at last. For the last few hours I had been the centre of attention. I had been frightened – not just for myself, but for my wife and my sons, but now I was on my own and I felt safe. I could now think about the last few hours, when my life had hung in the balance: the pains, my wife calling 999, the ambulance crew, their treatment and reassurance, the fast journey and the arrival at the Coronary Care Unit, followed by attention and treatment by the unit's staff. I began to think, as I drifted off to sleep, about the days when I first joined the medical profession back in 1975…

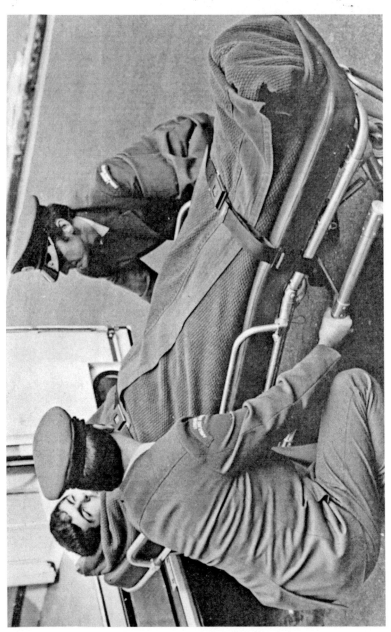

*A patient is stretchered aboard a London
Ambulance in the 1970s during training.*

PART I

Selection

I first saw the advertisement back in September 1974, and then again in a Sunday newspaper the following January.

AMBULANCE PERSONNEL REQUIRED – ALL AREAS OF LONDON
FULL TRAINING GIVEN – REWARDING CAREER
MALE / FEMALE – AGE 18 to 35 – FULL DRIVING LICENCE
APPLY TO PERSONNEL DEPT, LAS HEADQUARTERS,
WATERLOO ROAD, LONDON SE1

I thought about that advert for a few days.

"I need a change and a challenge," I kept saying to myself, "why not give it a go?" Eventually I plucked up the resolve to do something, applied for the necessary forms and waited...

Within a week the documents arrived. I spent an evening completing the questionnaire and reading leaflets that gave an insight into what was involved in training for and working in the ambulance service. Finaly, my mind was made up – I was going to give it a go. The following morning, on my way to work, I posted my reply.

Three weeks later, on a Saturday morning, the post arrived. There was a brown envelope with a *Greater London Council* crest stamped across the top. It was from the London Ambulance Service personnel department. I had been invited to a formal interview at 1015 hours 3rd February at New Malden Ambulance Station Area Office. I was to see a Mr Whiteside and was instructed to bring my driving licence.

I arranged for a day off work on the 3rd and duly arrived at New Malden in plenty of time for the interview. I was shown into a common room where several other applicants (one of whom was Bernie Allen, who I was to work with a couple of years later at a road traffic accident in which pop star Marc Bolan lost his life) to await my turn.

"Mr Kinsley, please come this way," a young woman said, pointing towards a door. "Please go straight in."

"Good morning Mr Kinsley, I'm Mr Whiteside, do please sit down."

He offered his hand. After a few informal questions about my family and the type of work that I was doing, he asked, "Why do you want to join the ambulance service?"

"I feel I want a change – a challenge," I replied.

"I will ask you several questions about the London area, for example, if I give you a postal district, you tell me if you can tell me the area it covers – do you understand?"

"Yes…" I replied nervously.

"South West Eight, South West Sixteen and South East Five, in that order, if you please."

"Battersea, Streatham and Camberwell sir."

"Good, good," he said, looking straight at me.

This went on for about twenty five minutes, questions about other London districts; how I would get from A to B

"I'll get that sorted today," I said, closing the door behind me... "Yes – yes – yes!" I repeated to myself as I walked down the corridor. "Yes – yes – yes!"

Within a few days I'd had my teeth repaired, my hair cut and arranged with an old friend, Sidney Oliver, to do some football training and some swimming at the local baths at least once a week. I was determined to lose the excess weight as soon as I could.

A week had passed, when another brown envelope arrived with the GLC logo on the front. I was apprehensive on tearing it open. Slowly, I pulled the folded white letter out. It read:

Mr John Kinsley,

re:- your medical examination that took place at County Hall, London SE1, on 20th February 1975, the medical examiner has stated that you are fit enough to commence training for the position of ambulanceman grade 2, therefore will you report to London Ambulance Service Headquarters Waterloo Road SE1 (Training Room – Ground Floor) on Monday 6th March at 0900hrs.

Bring with you your driving licence and dress in sensible clothing and footwear.

I informed the signal engineer at Croydon that I wished to terminate my employment with the department on Friday 3rd March 1975 and that from the following Monday I would be joining the London Ambulance Service. I had been with British Railways Signal Engineers Department since 1959, so a few farewells were said over the remaining days, and a few glasses tilted. I had made some good friends over the years and I won't ever forget them.

On Friday 3rd March 1975, I drove out of Redhill Railway yard for the very last time.

PART II

Training

This was the notice that greeted me as I entered the reception area at headquarters for the first time. With half an hour to spare, I climbed the stairway to find the canteen. Mug of tea in hand, I found a place amongst the other obviously new entrants, who were sitting apart from the uniformed personnel, who, we later learnt, were from the previous student intake.

At nine thirty, two uniformed ambulance-training officers entered room G-20 and introduced themselves to the forty new students, who were sitting in absolute silence.

"Good morning ladies and gentlemen, my name is Brian Streeter," said one, and pointing to his colleague added, "and this is Phil Saunders. We will be in charge of your training and assessment over the next eight weeks and Martin Woodward will be doing the driving training. You will meet him later this week."

Looking around the room, Phil Saunders then spoke for the first time.

"I see we have thirty eight men and two young ladies with us. I will tell you all now that not all of you will make it to the final selections in eight weeks time. Some of you will fall by the wayside by not reaching the standard required by the service. Some of you will make your own decision in that you are unsuitable for this type of work – it's not everyone's cup of tea."

Looking around the room again, he continued.

"Can everyone in this room honestly say to themselves that they could wipe some old ladies arse at two o'clock in the morning, clean her up, put her back to bed and make her comfortable. If you can, then you are the type of individual the service is looking for – it's not all glamour!"

He smiled. A few 'ums' and 'ahs' came from his audience as people shifted around in their seats.

"What I would like you to do for the next half an hour," Brian said, "is for each of you in turn, in your own words, to say a little about yourself, a brief description of your previous occupation or anything else you think might be of interest."

I discovered in the next half an hour that I was in the company of shopkeepers, bus drivers, office workers, an undertaker, a nurse, a solicitor, another two railwaymen and a stallholder from Petticoat Lane, the famous street market in the East End of London. From the start this chap had the 'gift of the gab', a great character but, unfortunately, like some of the others, he didn't make it to the end of the course...

The first week passed quite quickly. We had training in 'kinetics' or patient removals – from beds, the ground, vehicles and stretchers. We practised lifting trolley beds and chairs in and out of an ambulance and were taught about the proper use and storage of vehicle equipment. That first week ended with tuition about wound dressings for various open injuries and finally an oral examination of all the students in groups by Phil and Brian.

The loss of six of the students at the start of the second week was, explained Brian, because those individuals had not achieved the required standard. For those that remained, a daily assessment would be made and each student would be informed of his or her progress as the course continued.

At the mid-morning tea break and at lunchtime, we students sat about in groups, wondering who would be next to be asked to leave. It really was quite depressing, but I was determined to give it all that I had. It would have to be for a good reason, I decided – and only a disastrous mistake on my part would force my departure.

The remainder of the second week was very interesting. We were given training in anatomy and physiology, treatment of fractures, blood loss, head injuries, understanding the causes of unconsciousness, airway control and recovery positions. That Friday morning we had our first written exam, and after lunch, we took it in turns with Brian or Phil to go through each question and answer given.

Brian seemed happy with the answers I supplied.

"Fine John, keep it up," was all he said.

Week number three arrived with the loss of two more of our classmates. One, we were told, had to leave because of personal reasons and not because of his assessments. Again, the week was very interesting. We had a trip to a County Council warehouse at Tottenham to be fitted out with service uniforms and were told to report the following morning in full uniform for inspection, with lapel name labels to be worn whilst at the training school. The only alteration needed to my uniform was to the trouser length.

The journey to headquarters the following day was somewhat worrying. I pulled on a raincoat over my uniform, fearing that it might be spotted at a street collapse or a road traffic accident where I would be expected to render aid in some form or other. Fortunately, I made my journey's end without so much as a nosebleed!

In two regimental lines, 32 two of us were inspected for the first time in full uniform by the two instructors. Each made various comments as they walked up and down the two lines.

"Put your cap on properly," Brian said to me (I hate wearing hats) pulling it forward from the back of my head.

I heard Phil say in a loud voice to one of the girls standing behind me. "Susan, get that skirt altered by tomorrow morning. How the hell can you bend up and down in something like that?"

I must admit she did look nice in a pencil skirt, but it was obviously not suited to the work in hand.

"Right everyone, a very good turnout, very smart. Now dismiss and take your seats, we've a few things to go over before tea break," said Phil as he turned away towards his desk.

With everyone seated he continued.

"As from today we want you to sort yourselves out into eight groups of four. You will stay in these groups until the end of the course, so at tea break, you will have an extra half an hour to sort this out. In the groups, we want you to pick a leader, who will be changed weekly. You must advise Brian or myself who the leader is for each period."

Brian coughed and cleared his throat, then carried on.

"As from tomorrow morning, driving training will start. It has been arranged that you all to meet Mr Martin Woodward, the driving examiner and his colleagues in the underground car park at nine-thirty sharp. You will be divided into your groups and you will spend the whole day driving a variety of service vehicles, reporting back in this room at normal time on Thursday... and don't forget to have your driving licence on your person tomorrow."

Brian stood up and slowly walked around the classroom to the noticeboard, turning to the students.

"On the board here," he said pointing, "is a list for your information, a training schedule to take us through to the end of the course. I want you all to have a look at it and keep an eye on it in case we have to change the programme for any reason. As you will see by looking at the list, the remainder of this morning we will be learning the techniques of examining unconscious patients for injuries and fractures, immobilising limbs and how to use a scoop stretcher to move a casualty.

"This afternoon, be sharp back from lunch – we will be having two lectures, one from an officer of the London Fire Service and the second one after the afternoon tea break will be a lecture on emergency childbirth from Sister Ann Roberts of the obstetrics unit at St Thomas's hospital. Off you go now for your tea break and sort your groups out."

Looking up at the wall clock he said, "see you all back here at eleven o'clock sharp..."

My group consisted of Peter Green, Richard Yates (who in later years would be involved in the Embassy siege that captured a world audience on television) and Carole Young, the only other woman on the course. Peter was voted leader of the group for the remainder of the week, much to his disapproval.

The lectures that afternoon were met with great enthusiasm from the students. First the fire officer explained the basic set-up by the brigade personnel at an incident or accident scene, how to identify the officer in charge, the use of breathing apparatus sets, the right of entry to property, the working relationship between the brigade and the ambulance service, and the co-operation between the two services when removal of casualties is required.

The second lecture on obstetrics, given by Sister Ann Roberts, was met with equal enthusiasm. It included explanations of cleanliness required of patients and surroundings at the scene of a birth; how to give reassurance to the patient and relatives; clearance of the airway to the newborn; awkward births, including the umbilical cord around the infant's neck; breech births; blood loss and infusion; the retention of placenta; keeping baby warm; calling for assistance from the obstetrics unit via ambulance emergency control; removal of mother and child to a hospital unit, and above all, privacy and a professional attitude.

The driving course the following day went well as far as I was concerned. I and the other members of my group took it in turns to drive an ambulance from headquarters in Central London out towards Coulsdon in the southern suburbs and then back again to Waterloo. Later that day it was our turn to use a high-powered car, and again we took it in turns to drive out of town, this time a round trip along the M4 motorway, passing Heathrow airport towards Reading.

My group was down to three the following morning, Carole Young having failed the second part of the driving course. She was put back to join the new intake of students who had started the previous Monday.

The remainder of week three was taken up with more anatomy and physiology, treatment of fractures with films and slides of actual injuries. Again on the Friday we had a written exam, but this time as a group.

Week four arrived with the news that three more students had departed (including Carole), so we were now down to a class of twenty nine. Richard had agreed to be leader for the week and reported to the instructors. On his return, he informed Peter and I that we would be having two trips away from training school this week, one to the museum and then the mortuary at Guys Hospital and the second to a local casualty department.

The look around the hospital museum, with its exhibits and row upon row of specimen jars filled with various body parts immersed in preservative, was amazing and very instructive.

A little later, after a short tea break in the hospital canteen, my group, along with another, made our way through long corridors towards the quieter section of the old buildings at the rear of the hospital. I felt a little apprehensive on our approach to the swing doors leading to the mortuary.

"Come in gentlemen," was our greeting from a young lady dressed in operating theatre 'greens'. We followed her through a large room with about twenty large fridge doors on either side.

"This is the cold room where the deceased are kept until they are released to the undertakers – after we have completed our procedures."

We then came to an office area with a large picture window which looked out into a brightly lit room with a dozen marble topped tables, two of which were occupied with naked bodies, one male, one female.

"My name is Ann Reynolds and I am the assistant to Mr White the pathologist who is working here today. You can take your jackets off and leave them over there," she said pointing to a long row of hooks along the wall, "then follow me through to the work area."

We filed out in line behind the young assistant and crossed the large room to join Mr White, who was also dressed in theatre garb and standing with arms folded beside the table that held the naked female.

"Good morning to you all. My name is Mr White and welcome to the quietest part of the hospital," he said with a slight smile. "One of my duties here is to find the cause of death by examination and tests of the internal organs. In this case," he said looking down at the female in front of him, "this 42-year-old female died in the casualty department in the early hours of this morning after being brought in by ambulance. She was found unconscious at her home address and we need to discover the cause of death – that's our job. Was it foul play? An overdose? A terminal illness? Heart attack? Brain tumour? Or perhaps a combination of events led to the failure of her vital organs? He nodded towards his young assistant. "Miss Reynolds takes all the details by notes or by tape recordings as I progress through the examination, and then the final results as regards the cause of death are passed on through the system. – So gentlemen… I am going to start my examination, called a post mortem, of this lady now."

He looked down again as he continued.

"If any of you feel you would like to leave the room at any time, do so quietly and make your way back to the office area to await your colleagues." Then, looking up, he asked, "Any questions before I make a start?"

"Sir," I said, "how long does a post mortem take?"

"It depends on the case. It could be one or two hours, or in some cases even longer," the pathologist answered. As he was speaking, two white-coated porters arrived and removed the deceased male from the table onto a metal-topped trolley. I watched as they covered him in a sheet then slowly moved their load out into the holding cold room. A police officer arrived in the room shortly afterwards. He was there to observe and obtain any information about the sudden death of our forty-two year old female.

The pathologist welcomed the newcomer who joined our little group. For the following hour we stood fascinated by the clinical precision of the pathologist as he went about his work, all the time talking as he went from one procedure to the next, allowing his assistant time to record his findings. What I witnessed that day will remain with me forever.

Later we gave our thanks and bade our farewells as we trainees left the room to collect our coats from the office, then made our way back to meet the other students in the main hospital complex and onward to the headquarters training school.

Week four came to a close after my group had spent Thursday afternoon, and all day Friday at the casualty department of St Thomas's Hospital – on the south bank of the river Thames close to Westminster Bridge. Other groups from the course had been sent to various casualty receiving hospitals in central London, leaving us all to meet up again on the following Monday morning back at headquarters.

The casualty department at St Thomas's was very busy over the period of time we were there, with walking wounded coming and going – cuts to limbs and heads due to various reasons, earaches, stomach aches, eye injuries, plus, as one casualty sister put it, "the regulars".

We were looked at as 'greenhorns' by the ambulance crews who were arriving quite regularly with stretcher and chair cases to be placed in the treatment cubicles or taken straight to the wards.

"Enjoying it mate?" one crew member asked, "Don't worry, we've all been through it!" flicking my name tag with his fingers as he said it. I made a few good friends during that day and a half among the crews that were coming and going (one of them, John Palmer, I was later to crew-up with whilst doing my paramedic training in 1980).

On Friday morning, two emergency cases were brought into the resuscitation room for treatment by the crash room staff. The first was an elderly female, removed from the local river by a police launch and handed over to a waiting ambulance crew for transport to St Thomas's.

We students stood to one side as not to be in the way as the team went into action. The patient was moved across to a waiting trolley. She was stripped of all her wet clothes by nurses as other staff were going the business of setting up drip lines, allowing the remainder of the crash room staff room to attach monitor leads to the patients body. Thirty five minutes were spent on resuscitation attempts, but to no avail, the woman was certified dead by the two doctors in the room as the rest of the team stepped back from the trolley to start cleaning up the surrounding area.

It was the first time I had witnessed a death and another experience I would never forget.

The second crash room call that morning was for a twenty-three year old male who had been involved in a motorcycle road traffic accident close to the hospital. The team was standing ready for his arrival, and no time was lost by the crash team after the male was placed by the ambulance crew onto the crash room trolley. Again, his clothing was removed expertly by the waiting nurses, as the doctors were already making their assessment of the injuries received.

The patient was conscious, but in a lot of pain. He had severe injuries to both legs, and to one arm. After about half an hour, after the infusion lines had been applied, x-rays taken, monitor leads attached, and his limbs immobilised he was taken to the operating theatre for the necessary treatment.

Week five, and I was team leader. I reported to the instructors and was informed that the programme posted on the board in the classroom would be changed for the following Friday, where mock examinations would take place, and would I advise my group. Team leaders were alsotold that progress was pleasing, and the feedback from the casualty departments that the students had attended was more than satisfactory. Monday and Tuesday was taken up with teachings of the cardiovascular system, with signs and symptoms of heart failure, followed by lectures on the central nervous system, with further details explained with the help of slides and diagrams.

Wednesday and Thursday all the groups spent the time in the radio telephone training room on the first floor, learning the phonetic alphabet, use of the two way radio's, and airway procedure, with the promise from the instructor that we could have another short lesson in the final week before the R/T exam. Friday arrived along with the apprehension of the forthcoming mock exam. We spent two and a half hours on the written paper, after which we were told to go into the instructors office one at a time in alphabetical order to obtain our results. Those left waiting their time to be called were told to do revision until all students had been seen, those leaving the instructors office went straight to the canteen for tea and a cigarette. My turn came, I was shaking as I entered the office and told to sit down by Brian who was sitting behind a large desk sifting through the examination papers.

"What do you think of the course John?" was the thing he said as I sat down.

"Fine, enjoying it," I replied.

"How do you think you done with the paper?" he asked, holding my paperwork a few inches above the desktop.

I waited a few moments before replying, "I was not too sure about some of the questions on the central nervous system, as for the rest of the questions, yes, I was happy." Clearing his throat, Brian said, "you do need to do some revision, the nervous system, and signs and symptoms of heart failure, so get your head into the books, there is only a few weeks to go, and you won't have a second chance, but I must add, your doing well, very pleased with your practical work, and your attitude." "Anything to add?" he said turning to Phil who was sitting in the corner taking notes.

"No not really, just keep up the good work John, and don't forget the revision," ending with "off you go for your cuppa, and send the next man in please." The conversation in the canteen revolved around the previous three hours, and everyone was certainly relieved that it was over which showed in the talk and body language.

Surrey Commercial Docks, situated in south east London was the venue for the students at the start of week six, where several instructors set up mock accident sites in and around the old warehouse buildings. From a central meeting point in the docks area, the groups in turn were sent out in a ambulance to attend to the mock situations that had been set them, from collapsed casualties on a warehouse roof, trapped and unconscious patients in overturned cars (vehicles supplied by the local council), removal of a spinal injury patient from a third floor machine shop, using a fire escape as the only means of exit. Returning to the meeting point with the casualty on board the ambulance to be assessed on the treatment and safe removal by a waiting instructor. Whilst other instructors toured the docks area with clipboards in hand walked around the accident sites marking their comments down as each group arrived at the various scenes to be assessed on their approach, action, and treatment at site, with finally the removal procedure to the waiting ambulance. In all we spent three days at the docks. With the groups taking it in turns to be the victims, and with Brian Streeter using his skills to apply makeup to make the injuries all the more realistic to the attending trainee medics.

Back at headquarters on Thursday we were split into pairs again for mock accident situations, this time in the lower garage area under the main building. Each student took it in turns to be the ambulance attendant for the task facing them. The casualty (another student) had make-up applied to simulate the symptoms of an inllness or injury, and also a label attached somewhere about his person, giving a full description of signs and symptoms in the case of an illness, or injuries received in the case of an accident; it also stated whether or not the patient was conscious.

I was quite nervous as my turn quickly came around to be the attendant to the next call. Not knowing what to expect, I arrived in the garage area in almost total darkness. With torch in hand, borrowed from a nearby ambulance, I found my patient lying face down in front of a service Land Rover. Bending down, I shone the torch onto the label that was pinned to the student's overall. It informed me:

I'm a middle-aged male, knocked over by a car, head injury, unconscious and a compound fracture of my right femur.

"So what's your action going to be John?" Phil Saunders asked, bending down beside me.

"First, I'll check for a pulse; if present then aspirate if needed and maintain the airway. If no pulse, start resuscitation, then check pupils for dilation regarding the obvious head injury. Then, starting from the head, work down the body, checking for other injury sites and deformities. I would dress the head injury and check for a pulse in the right foot. If no pulse present – use traction on the leg to reinstate pulse pressure, then splint the leg. Use the scoop stretcher and load onto the trolley bed, then into the ambulance."

Having answered, I stood up.

"And your mate, what would he be doing whilst this was going on?" Phil asked.

Pausing for a moment I replied, "he would see if the driver was all right, then assist me, in the resuscitation if it was needed, plus get the splints, the scoop and trolley bed, so they were close at hand, also help me with the traction if it was necessary, help in general really."

"Sounds fine to me, let's see you do it," said Phil, turning and walking away to make his observations from a distance. With another student as my crewmate we set about the task that had been set us, and within a short while we had gone through my set plan and the treatment procedures, ending by loading the make believe casualty onto the waiting ambulance.

"Right, make your way back upstairs, go and have some lunch, and meet back in the classroom at one-thirty sharp," was all Phil said as he appeared at the back of the ambulance.

After lunch, and on a one to one basis each student was debriefed by the instructor that had assessed their mock accident scenario. Phil sat behind his desk glancing down at the clipboard as I entered the room.

"Sit," he said without up. I sat as ordered, and for a few moments more he ran his pencil up and down the paperwork in front of him. Putting the board down on the desktop he looked up at me.

"How do you think you got on this morning downstairs?"

"Alright I think," was all I could say in reply.

Looking down again at the paperwork on the desk he continued.

"You did quite well, but work a little bit slower when you examine an unconscious patient, you did it much too fast. You can miss injury sites etc if they are not awake and able to tell you where they hurt. Apart from that – well done."

After a little smalltalk about the training course in general, I made my way back to join my colleagues in the classroom, where the talk revolved around the mock accident scenes that we had faced that morning.

Week six came to a close after further training in the use of poles and canvases – Parratt – Scoop – Furley – and Neil Robertson type stretchers, the ambulance trolley bed, the patient carrying chair, and the storage and use of rescue equipment.

Week seven started with the loss of another student, who we learnt had resigned from the course late on the previous Friday, so we were now down to 28 in number. The fear of failure still hung over us as we faced our final two weeks.

We watched films and slide shows which informed us about signs, symptoms and treatments for head injuries, epilepsy, cerebral/vascular accidents (i.e. strokes – known as CVAs for short) which took us through to Tuesday afternoon, when group discussions with one of the instructors followed.

The remainder of the week seven was taken up again with lectures, more slide shows and group discussions on the subjects of the cardiovascular, respiratory, autonomic and central nervous systems, with treatments for epilepsy, asthma, and heart attack victims, followed by individual practical tests on a manikin for full resuscitation procedures including closed chest cardiac massage.

My evenings at home that week and the following weekend were taken up with revision as I did my utmost to answer questions fired at me by my wife, who did her best with the medical terminology facing her as she progressed through the course notes and manuals in front of her.

Finals week had arrived, the tension showing as we students jostled around the noticeboard to mentally note how the week's program had been arranged for each group. Peter, Richard, and myself had to report to the radio room for the radio telephone exam that morning, and after a few hiccups with the phonetic alphabet at the start of the test all three of us managed to pass the required test level by the lunchtime.

In the afternoon, my group met up with a driving instructor in the lower garage area, where taking it in turn we went out in a high-powered Ford Granada to be assessed on 'defensive driving' in heavy traffic conditions. The three of us were told on our return to the classroom that the driving assessment had been successful.

I went home that Monday evening pleased with the days results, but mentally exhausted, knowing that further revision would be the evening's entertainment.

Tuesday morning, and my group was being assessed for bed removals, blanket and stretcher work, taking it in turns to be the patient as the other two carried out the operations set for them by the onlooking instructor. After lunch we had an afternoon filled with mock accident situations down in the lower garage area – this time for a final assessment of each individual by two training officers.

With clipboards in hand, the officers watched and made notes as each student approached the site, made his appraisal and informed the officers of his intentions for treatment.

My turn eventually came. This time the garage area was fully lit as I approached my make-believe patient, who was sitting up against the garage wall. *Middle-aged male, collapsed with chest pains, known heart condition, conscious, cyanosis visible, sweating, and cold and clammy* was the information printed on the card pinned to his jacket.

"What are you going to do Mr Kinsley?" one of the instructors asked.

"Loosen his collar, give reassurance, ask if he has pains anywhere else, ask if he has taken any pills or spray that has been prescribed..."

"Such as..." the instructor interrupted.

"Trinitrate – for angina." I replied.

"And if he hasn't?"

"I would ask if he had some on him, and if so, place one under the tongue, or use the spray to help alleviate the pain. I would administer oxygen, take the pulse, wipe his brow and neck and keep him warm." I answered.

"And how would you transport him, and how often would you take the pulse?" the instructor asked as he moved closer to me. Suspecting a catch question I took a few seconds before I replied.

"I would take and note the pulse and rate of breathing every few minutes, as regards the removal, on a trolley bed in a sitting position."

"Plenty of reassurance?" he inquired.

"Yes plenty," I said turning to face him.

"Thank you Mr Kinsley that will be all for now, make your way back to the classroom, and thank you once again."

As I walked back along the corridors towards the classroom I was thinking, 'that can't be it, it was over too quickly, there's got to be a catch somewhere...'

"How did it go John?" Phil Saunders asked as I entered the classroom.

"Yeah, fine – I think – just a few questions by the instructors, there was no removal to an ambulance or any treatment," I said as I took my seat.

"Well, there wouldn't be would there?" he said with a smile, "You were on your own and you have been doing patient removals all morning, remember?"

The day finished with a lecture on compulsory orders and patient removals with regard to the Mental Health Act, after which it was time for home, dinner and further revision.

A lecture on emergency childbirth by Phil and Brian, followed by group revision with a question and answer period with the instructors led up to the lunch break on Wednesday morning. We knew that on our return from the break we would be faced with the final written examination.

I made my way out on to the verandah at the back of the canteen after my refreshments to enjoy a cigarette, where I was joined by Carole Young, the student from my group who had been put back a course after her failure on the driving test.

" Hi John, how's it going?" she said putting her arm around my shoulder.

"Dreading this afternoon, got the written paper, I bloody wish it was all over," I said ,turning to face her and offering a cigarette at the same time.

"Thanks," Carole said, taking one and lighting it. "I'm leaving today," she stated matter-of-factly, blowing a plume of smoke into the air.

"Leaving … why?" I asked her with a quizzical expression.

"It's the driving, I can't deal with the heavy traffic, it just makes me a nervous wreck. It's not going to work for me John, so I'm going back to work with me mum and dad in their shoe shop at Clapham. It's a shame, I like the job, but it's just one of those things, I just cant cope with the pressure."

"Have they given you a rough time downstairs?" I inquired.

"No, not at all, they have been very fair," she continued, exhaling more smoke, "they have tried over and over again with extra driving through the city and down to the suburbs, but it's no good, I just cant get it together – so it's back to the normal world for me." She gave an embarrassed grin.

We stayed on the veranda enjoying the spring sunshine, the small talk and another cigarette before we had to go our separate ways.

"Must go Carole, you take care now, look after yourself and all the best," I said, turning to make my exit.

"You too John, you'll do well, I just know it," she said leaning forward and lightly kissing me on the cheek. "See you around no doubt, and good luck," she called after me as I walked back towards the main building. I raised my arm in silent reply.

Brian welcomed us back to the classroom as we took our seats at the desks that had been separated into lines several feet apart, obviously placed to prevent any form of 'over the shoulder' cheating for the forthcoming exam. He stood up to make an address after everyone had settled, and quietness enveloped the room.

"Before we start," he said looking around at the seated students, "all of you here have done very well so far this week, nobody has failed any of the assessments since Monday, so keep it up. I won't say good luck for the exam this afternoon, because you all know the answers, just take your time with the paper and think – don't rush the questions."

Holding a sheet of paper in the air, he carried on.

"You have one and a half hours to complete the exam, it's a multi-choice answer paper with four tick boxes to each question. If you make a mistake, make it clear at the side of the box as to what your final answer will be, when you have finished, bring the question and answer papers to my desk as quietly as you can, then make your way to the canteen for tea, returning back here at three-thirty sharp."

With that, he walked up and down the gangways, placing the exam papers face down on the desktops until everyone was supplied and ready to start.

The multi-choice paper covered all subjects from head and chest injuries, severe haemorrhaging, the different types of fractures, burns, a few questions on emergency childbirth, but the emphasis mostly on signs and symptoms of sudden illness.

When finished, and after reading through my answers to the questions a few times, I placed my paperwork on Brian's desk as he had requested, then made my way to the canteen to join the couple of students who had made their exit a few minutes earlier.

Brian made no comment as regards the examination on our return to the classroom at three-thirty, just saying that everyone had completed the paper in the allotted time. Wednesday 's course day finished following a lecture from Phil, about major accident procedures, the duties of the first ambulance crew to the scene, the numbers of casualties, the positioning of the emergency vehicles, reporting to the other two emergency services at site, and reporting back to control at Red Base. It was an interesting lecture after a long, and in most cases a very stress-filled day.

On Thursday morning we were told collectively by the instructors that all twenty-eight students had passed the written examination. The announcement was met with jubilation – but we still had a full days assessment in front of us, to include the oral examination by the doctor attached to the service, along with two instructors from another intake course. My turn for the audience with the doctor came halfway through the morning when my name was called by a young lady whose job for the day was to maintain a steady flow of students to and from the interview rooms.

"Hello Mr Kinsley, please take a seat," was my greeting from a friendly-looking woman sitting between two uniformed officers behind a large polished desk. She looked up from the folder she was holding. "My name is Doctor Jennings, on my left is instructor Don Wilkinson, and on my right is his colleague Roger Masters. We will be asking you a few questions, so take your time in answering and if you are not certain of the way to explain anything do say so, and we will attack the question from a different angle. Do you understand?" She gave me a broad smile.

"Yes doctor," I replied quietly.

After replacing the folder on the desk, and folding her arms across her chest, she asked me.

"What is meant by the term *pneumothorax* and how would you treat the condition?"

Clearing my throat and crossing my legs, I answered slowly.

"Following an open injury to the chest area, air is allowed to enter the pleural cavities causing a lung to collapse…"

"If the patient was conscious how would you expect them to look?" the doctor interrupted.

"Distressed, in shock with difficulty in breathing and possibly cyanosis," I answered quietly.

Roger Masters spoke in a high-pitched voice.

"And the treatment John?"

Again I answered quietly.

"Seal the wound, treat with oxygen and if possible transport in the upright position."

Several seconds elapsed before the other instructor Don Wilkinson asked.

"What is Dypnoea, John?"

"It's difficult or laboured breathing sir," I said looking at him.

Again several more seconds passed before the doctor looked up from where she had been taking notes and asked.

"What's the resting rate of breathing for an adult, and a child, also what's the make up of gas's in expired air?"

Shifting my position in the chair, I took a deep breath before answering.

"An adult's breathing rate is between fifteen and twenty times a minute, a childs between twenty and forty times a minute." Taking another deep breath I continued, "expired air is made up of four percent of carbon dioxide – sixteen percent of oxygen – and eighty percent of nitrogen, ma'am."

For the next ten minutes the trio asked questions in turn, ending with the doctor asking me what type of wound would I expect from a stabbing injury. After answering, she asked if I had any questions to ask before the interview was terminated.

"Just one – ma'am, can you tell me how I have done?"

"Fine – but you will be officially advised in due course and if that's all Mr Kinsley, thank you very much, you can now make your way back to your classroom."

Back at the classroom I joined the others, who were sitting around in groups, still doing revision. I sat down with a terrible empty feeling in the pit of my stomach – and it wasn't hunger.

After a short lunch break, those of us who had already seen the doctor sat in a group with the instructors, going through the questions and answers given at the morning's interview. Peter Green from my group was the last student to see the doctor, and on his return the instructors dismissed us all for an extended tea break, telling us to report back by four o'clock. With gut feelings and cigarettes in hand most of the students strolled about the veranda in the afternoon spring sunshine, deep in thought like myself, going over the events of the day.

A deadly hush greeted Phil and Brian as they entered the classroom sharp at four o'clock to face the seated students. Brian cleared his throat with a small cough.

"Congratulations are in order to you all..."

Before he could continue, a loud cheer went up from his captivated audience as the pent-up pressure released itself.

"Shhh! Not too loud," he said with a very wide grin.

"You all passed with flying colours. Well done from Phil and myself, you have worked very hard. Has it been worth it?"

"Yes!" we shouted in unison.

Phil moved forward to speak. "Well done everyone, you deserve it. Now... as for tomorrow morning, we all meet here at nine o'clock where we will have a debrief on the course, plus a question and answer period after which you will be told what your duties will be as from next Monday when you go out into the big wide world. Some of you will be working from the headquarters accident station, others will be working from the headquarters on white work, some of you will be stationed at the satellite accident stations at Bloomsbury and Smithfield and all of you will be working for the next few weeks under the instructions of a on-road training officer. Understand now that you are still on a probationary period – today is only the beginning – there is still a lot to learn and put into practice, so be very careful.

Enough of that for the moment, if you decide to have a celebration drink tomorrow – I have heard the rumours – Brian and I will be more than happy to join you, but remember ... no drinking and driving, so make other arrangements to get home ... and bring a change of clothing – no uniforms to be worn in the pubs.

So there we are... off you go and tell your family and friends of your good news and we will see you all back here at nine sharp tomorrow – and well done."

With holdalls full of civilian clothes, the students turned up at nine o'clock sharp on the last day in the training room at headquarters. Following a course debrief and a short question and answer period we were informed of our forthcoming postings. I was to be crewed up with Peter Green from my group, and our instructions were to report to training officer Alan Richardson at Bloomsbury accident ambulance station at Russell Square in time to take over duty on the vehicle

Bloomsbury One accident and emergency ambulance at 1400 hours on the following Wednesday afternoon.

After all the students had been issued with a list of telephone numbers to be contacted in the event of being unable to report for duty for any reason, Peter and I got together to make our arrangements for meeting up prior to the arrival at Bloomsbury for the first time. Neither of us wanted to arrive at the station on our own.

The celebration drink with a little food was held at the New Crown & Cushion pub in Westminster Bridge Road at Waterloo, just a small distance from the headquarters building, and along with Phil and Brian the 28 students, all now in civilian clothing, enjoyed the few hours together for the last time.

PART III

Bloomsbury Accident & Emergency Training Station

Wednesday arrived as a wet, cold and very windy day, winter had returned with a vengeance. Peter and I arrived in good time at Russell Square to find a parking space close to the ambulance station. At least the rain had turned to a light drizzle as we approached the station for the first time.

"How do you feel Pete?" I asked, with just a few yards to go.

"You want to know the truth, I'm shit scared," he replied. "And you?"

"Yeah, the same, I feel sick," I said to him, as we walked into an empty garage area – both the Bloomsbury vehicles must still be out on the road.

"Hello lads, I'm Alan Richardson, your training officer for the next couple of weeks," was our greeting from a thirty-ish, six-foot-tall, well-groomed officer as we entered the garage.

"Glad you're nice and early, it gives us a bit of time to look around your new home for the next couple of months. I'll show you both around as soon as you put your kit in the mess room."

He held a door open for us to enter the inner building. After informal introductions had been made, the officer gave Peter and I the grand tour of the small ambulance station.

It had originally been a fire station before the fire brigade moved to new premises further up the road at Euston. The messroom-cum-watchroom was small but comfortably furnished, a large coloured street map almost covered one wall, two telephones graced a table below the map layout, one being red (the emergency call land line from Red Base control at headquarters) the other grey (an outside line for normal incoming calls only). Alongside the telephones were the message pads and LA-4 emergency forms that are filled out as information is passed down from ambulance control via the red telephone. Along a small hallway were doors leading off to a store holding ambulance equipment, spare dressings, splints, and a large pile of clean red blankets. Another door led us to the compact toilet and washroom area and finally a back door that led to the rear of the garage with a collection of mops, buckets, brooms and a hose reel – all used for the vehicle cleaning. Alan called Peter and I back into the mess-room to join him for a pot of tea he had made, and we sat around making small talk whilst awaiting the return of *Bloomsbury One* back on station.

We learnt that the *Bloomsbury Three* ambulance was a two shift vehicle, early and late turns only and although based at the station it returned to headquarters every night, where it was garaged ready for use by the on-coming morning crew.

At 1435 hours, *Bloomsbury One* returned and Alan instructed Peter and myself to carry out the vehicle equipment check immediately the ambulance was back in the garage.

This is a check carried out by all ambulance crews on their commencement of duty, to replenish dressings or equipment used on the previous call and to replace any soiled blankets that may be on board. The crew carry out the check against a list, making a mark against each piece of equipment as it is examined, knowing that at the finish, the ambulance is fully equipped and ready for service. After this, the duty driver checks the oil, water and petrol levels, followed by a test of the tyre pressures. While this is going on, the attendant for the day sweeps and mops the saloon floor and generally prepares the ambulance.

As I performed that first vehicle check on *Bloomsbury One* I felt physically sick, knowing that any time now we could be turning out to answer any emergency that Red Base dealt us, and I could tell that Peter felt exactly the same, he was quiet, and very pale.

The off-going crew, one of whom I recognized as a student on an earlier course to mine at training school shouted their farewells as they left the station. Alan peered into the back of the ambulance as I had just finished cleaning the floor.

"I've just made a coffee for the pair of you," he said. "I hope you've done the vehicle check alright. If not, you're due a bollocking first-class." He smiled. "Now off you go for your coffee while I have a quick look around."

With that, Peter and I made for the mess room and awaited his return.

Making no comment, Alan joined us ten minutes later, picking up drink from the table he claimed a comfortable looking chair in the corner.

"Who's going to be the attendant today?" he inquired looking at us in turn.

"We tossed a coin, and I'm going to attend today," I said, with the butterflies returning.

Moving his position, Alan turned to face Peter.

"I will drive on the first call Peter, so you get an idea, then we will see from there. Same for John tomorrow, when he will be driving. OK?"

We both nodded our agreement in unison. Alan continued.

"Sometime this evening we will have to refuel at HQ, Peter. On the gauge it's just below three quarters full and we never let it get below half full."

Again, without comment, we both nodded our reply.

Turning to face me, Alan said "Fill out the LA-1 form John, and put my name down as being on the crew. The same goes when you fill out an LA-4, put my name down in the bottom left hand corner, stating in brackets 'training officer in attendance'. Alright? Now, the pair of you, it's not the end of the world, it's a good job that you're doing and in a few days time your feel a lot better," he gave a slight smile, "we've all been through it."

[NB. The LA-1 form, is the daily service running sheet for the ambulance, stating number of patients carried, walking, chair or stretcher cases, mileage covered, and the crew names. The LA-4 form, is the accident and emergency sheet, recording each call address, the times, patient details, injuries received, and treatment carried out, receiving hospital, and again the attending crew's names, ambulance number and call-sign.]

Bloomsbury Three crew, along with their training officer returned to station as Alan was giving Peter and myself a rundown on his career with the service, from leaving the armed forces up until the present day working with the training school.

"Hello Tom," Alan greeted the other officer as he entered the room, leaving his crew to replenish the items they had used on their last call, which they had received over the radio as they were travelling from headquarters after the early-turn crew change.

"Hi Alan, finally made it," was the officer's reply as he closed the door behind him.

"Put the kettle on John," Alan asked me as his colleague placed a clipboard on the table, slid out a chair and sat down.

"Yeah, will do," I said, getting up and making my way over to the kitchen units. I had filled the kettle, switched it on, and was just preparing the cups when I nearly had a heart attack as the station area was filled with ear shattering alarm bells. The repeater bell in the garage and the red phone in the mess room also sprung into life with continuous ringing until the receiver was lifted by the officer sitting at the table.

"Yes – Yes, got that," he said, repeating the incoming message back to the controller at Red Base before replacing the handset back on it's cradle.

"One for your lot Alan. A woman fallen from a number 196 bus outside Kings Cross Station, the police are on scene." Tom waved the endorsed LA-4 form in the air and I grabbed it on the way to the door.

The wind and rain had ceased with just a glimmer of sunshine trying to break through the clouds as Alan eased *Bloomsbury One* out into the heavy traffic through Tavistock Square and onwards to Euston and Kings Cross. With the two tones blaring and the blue lights flashing, traffic eased over to make a path for the oncoming ambulance as Alan drove at a steady pace throughout the seven minute journey with no sharp turns or severe braking, showing his truly professional approach to emergency vehicle driving.

My first ever casualty was attended by a very nervous ambulance attendant. With heart pounding, I made my way towards a policeman who was waving me over to his car where the patient was sitting on the passenger seat with her feet resting on the pavement. A deep laceration, about six inches long down the side of her right leg calf muscle, allowed blood to flow freely. I removed the hand-held dressing she had been given, made a quick assessment of the wound, then re-dressed the injury with two 'number three' bandages.

"Have you hurt yourself anywhere else," I asked.

"Just a small graze on my right hand – I feel such a fool," she replied as she raised her hand for my inspection, at the same time showing her embarrassment at the attention she was receiving in front of a small crowd of onlookers. After cleaning the dirt away from the scratches on her hand, Peter and I loaded the young woman onto the trolley bed, then onboard the ambulance, followed by a slow journey to the nearest casualty hospital, which was University College, about a mile and a half from Kings Cross. At the hospital, after finding a cubicle for our patient, Alan showed us the procedures for booking in casualties to the reception area. He helped us re-loading and making up the trolley bed with blankets, in his eyes a much neater way.

It took me about ten minutes to fill in the details on the form LA-4. Alan walked over to me and, taking the clipboard from my hand, said, "Let's have a look John ... Looks fine, don't forget to put my name in the bottom left hand corner." He handed the board back to me. "Just one other thing young man before we move off ... where's your hat?"

"I left it back at the station, sorry," I replied, embarrassed.

Taking a deep breath Alan said, "Consider yourself bollocked. Don't let it happen again. Understand?"

"It won't," I sighed.

"Right, let's make a move… you can drive Peter." The officer moved across to make room for Peter to slide in behind the steering wheel.

I picked up the microphone.

"Red Base – Bloomsbury One – Red Base Over."

"Bloomsbury One Go Ahead."

"Green At The UCH Over."

"Thank You Bloomsbury One, Green Time 1704 RTB."

"RTB Roger."

"Red Base Out."

Peter slowly pulled our ambulance out of the hospital grounds to join the evening rush hour traffic as the rain started yet again, the overcast sky causing an early night-full. With the heavy congestion, we had travelled only a short distance when the radio telephone came to life interrupting the small talk between the three of us.

"Bloomsbury One Report."

"Bloomsbury One Green At Russell Square Over."

"Thank You Bloomsbury One, Got A Call Red Accident If Your Ready For Details Over."

"Go Ahead Over"

"It's A call Red Accident to the Ladies Toilets at Leicester Square WC2. Female Collapsed. Timed to you at 1717 hours. My initials Delta Foxtrot, Bloomsbury One Over."

I read the call back to the controller, ending with my initials before replacing the microphone Back in it's cradle as Alan leaned through the connecting door from the rear saloon.

"Now take your time Peter, don't go mad, nice and easy through the traffic, I'll tell you which way to go," he said as he made himself comfortable in the doorway.

"Switch the blue lights on, John you can work the two tone switch."

With the warnings activated, the ambulance eased out of the stationary rush hour traffic.

"Go all the way around the square Peter, take the second left, keep on with the horns John, let them know were coming through."

Under Alan's direction, *Bloomsbury One* made progress past the British Museum, down Shaftesbury Avenue, across Charing Cross Road, and into Leicester Square. It was amazing to witness how in heavy traffic a pathway was created for the oncoming ambulance, throughout the journey the noise from the two tones in the cab was deafening as the echo's bounced back and forth from the surrounding buildings.

"That's it Peter, nice and steady, over there on your left, park up on the kerb, blue lights off, and switch the hazards on," Alan said as he was turning around to make his exit from the rear doors. Taking with us a carrying chair, blanket, and first aid satchel we were met at the top of the stairway leading down to the toilets by a plainclothes woman police officer who led us on to a cubicle where a young dishevelled female was laying at the side of a dirty toilet bowl, face down and unconscious. At her side were two used syringes with traces of a brown liquid still evident.

After kneeling down to make a quick assessment I turned to Peter and asked, "Pete, can you get the aspirator, her airway's full of vomit."

Within a minute Peter was back, and with the suction unit we managed to clear a large amount of fluid, allowing me room to insert an airway to prevent the tongue from falling back and blocking the windpipe. All the time Peter and I were working on the casualty, Alan stood back, directing other toilet user's away from our area, but still in a position to make his observations. After a while, we loaded the young lady into the ambulance, and placed her in the recovery position on the trolley bed when Alan joined us.

"Breathing alright John?" he asked leaning forward to take a look.

"Yes," I replied, moving to one side to make room for him.

"Good, give some oxygen and keep an eye on her. I'll be up front with Peter. Do you think we should put a blue call in?" he asked, looking around at me.

"Yea, I think so, I said moving across to attach the oxygen mask to the patient.

Peter climbed behind the steering wheel, and within a second, with blue lights back on, the Ambulance was rejoining the rush hour traffic, as Alan lifted the microphone to place the call.

"Priority."

"Go Ahead Priority."

"Bloomsbury One – Blue Call – Middlesex Hospital, Unconscious Female – ETA , Five Minutes Over"

I heard the Red Base controller repeat the request Alan had made over the R/T, then the two tones burst back into life as Peter was directed back along Charing Cross Road and on towards the Middlesex casualty department. At the hospital we were met by the duty casualty sister who led us through her department to the brightly lit crash room, where two doctors and a couple of nurses were waiting.

"She's one of our regulars, a known addict," the sister said as she and the doctors moved forward to help slide the patient across to the waiting hospital trolley. I stood there watching for a couple of minutes as the team went about their routine.

"New crew Alan?" the sister asked, as he entered the room and handed the two syringes wrapped in plastic bags to the sister.

"Yes, their first day today, Bloomsbury crew," he replied to the sister.

"Be seeing a lot of you two over the next few weeks then," she said turning to face Peter and me.

"For your records," she continued, "she goes by the name of Jacqueline Rose, aged eighteen, of no fixed abode and a known heroin addict. It's the second time she's been in this week, she discharged herself from here last Monday afternoon."

I heard the suction unit being used in the background as Jacqueline started to vomit again as she regained consciousness. The stench that filled the room was awful as the three of us turned to make our exit. I joined Peter and Alan back at the ambulance after I had booked our patient in at reception. Climbing onboard, I settled down to do the paperwork.

Alan addressed the pair of us.

"Well done, a good job. One thing though, you forgot the syringes when you removed the casualty from the scene, remember to put anything that you may think has been used or taken into a bag, and give it to the casualty staff on your arrival, it could be important and save a lot of time. OK?"

We both nodded our agreement.

"As for your driving Peter, very good, if you continue like that you should have no problem, again just remember, no need to go like a bat out of hell, fast yes, but steady – a nice even pace and let them hear and see you in plenty of time. As I said, well done."

With the paperwork completed, I contacted Red Base on the R/T, stating we were green at the Middlesex, in reply, they returned us to station.

That first evening at Bloomsbury we had another two overdose calls from station to the Soho Area, where on both occasions the patients were removed to the Middlesex Hospital and received as known addicts. The last call on that first day was received on station just as we were preparing to hand over to the night shift, who were due on station in about ten minutes. Red Base called on the emergency line and instructed us to attend a road traffic accident in Guildford Street, just a few hundred yards from the station. On our arrival, it transpired to be a minor shunt between two cars resulting in a damage only with no casualties, so within ten minutes of receiving the call we were back on station, completing the days paperwork and handing *Bloomsbury One* over to the incoming night crew. Like the early-turn crew, I recognized them as students from the previous training course to mine who were now on the road, unsupervised.

Peter and I climbed into my car and sat there for a few minutes, inhaling smoke from cigarettes and going briefly over the events of the last eight hours.

"How do you think it went Pete?" I asked as I stubbed out my cigarette in the ashtray.

"I think it went pretty well, although on that first call when the bell's went, I nearly shit myself!"

"Me too… We must have looked a right pair of bloody idiots to Alan, but there again he must see it all the time with the new blokes. I bet he has a right old laugh when he gets home."

"Yeah, I bet," Peter said, leaning forward to stub out his cigarette.

Moving the car away from Bloomsbury we headed towards Waterloo Bridge, across the Thames into South London and home.

Thursday was a beautiful spring day, the wind had at last dropped, and it had turned very warm. Alan was there to meet us on station as Peter and I arrived in plenty of time to get ready to take over from the early-turn crew, who unlike the previous day, were on station, and had just finished cleaning the ambulance. The off-going crew shouted out their farewell as Peter and I boarded the ambulance to start the necessary vehicle check.

"All done?" Alan inquired as we entered the mess room after the check.

"Yeah, just one dirty blanket to change, then we're all complete," Peter answered as he made his way across the room and out towards the storeroom.

Turning to me he asked, "Engine and fuel alright John?"

"Fine, got just over three quarters showing on the petrol gauge," I replied as I made my way to the sink to wash my hands.

"Good, we will fill up some time this evening at headquarters."

Alan got up from his chair to pour out three cups of tea as Peter re-entered the room after putting the clean blanket onboard the ambulance.

"How do the pair of you feel after your first day on the road yesterday," Alan asked with a smile as he sat down and placed his cup on the table. Peter looked at me as I spoke for the pair of us.

"Alright, but still a bit nervous though," I said joining the other two around the table.

"Good, being nervous keep's you on your toes," he said, again with a broad grin. Replacing his cup on the table after taking a sip he continued, "I've been on to Red Base and told them we are fully manned, they normally phone through at the changeover times to see that all crews are on station, so as I said before, it's important that you report for duty before your appointed time."

Peter and I both nodded our agreement.

"As for today," Alan continued, "Peter you will be the attendant so get your clipboard and LA-1 ready, John you will be driving, but as yesterday I will drive on the first call, then you can take over – OK?"

"Yes," I replied.

"This afternoon, because it's nice and warm, we will be in shirtsleeve order, so leave your coats on the vehicle – and don't forget your hats," he said turning to look at me.

The next hour was spent on station duties, cleaning and polishing the mess room floor. I was out sweeping the garage area when the bells went for the first time on our shift. The call was for an urgent hospital transfer of a serious head injury patient from U.C.H. casualty department to the Atkinson Morley Hospital at Cottenham Park, just outside Wimbledon in South West London. The patient, a twenty two year old female, had received a subdural haemorrhage injury after falling down a flight of stairs at her workplace.

In the hospital casualty department, Peter and I loaded the young female onto our trolley bed, then out to the waiting ambulance. With a doctor and nurse escort aboard, *Bloomsbury One* pulled out into afternoon traffic with blue lights and two tones blaring as Alan, behind the wheel, headed south towards the river Thames.

At a steady pace, the ambulance weaved through the early evening rush hour traffic, across Lambeth Bridge, along through the Vauxhall one-way system and onto the Wandsworth Road. Several times during the journey, without turning around, Alan asked the escorts if everything was alright in the back and that they were not being thrown about as he had to manoeuvre the vehicle around almost stationary traffic. After a run of just over twenty-five minutes, Alan eased *Bloomsbury One* off the Kingston By-Pass at the Coombe Lane roundabout, took a left at Copse Hill at the side of Wimbledon Common, and approached our designated hospital on the right side sitting amongst a beautiful array of cherry blossom trees in full bloom.

Peter and I unloaded the trolley bed and with our escorts and instructor followed a smart uniformed porter through a maze of corridors to 'Kent' ward, where medical staff were obviously awaiting our arrival. With their help, we moved our patient to a larger than normal size bed surrounded by several items of medical equipment, including a resuscitation trolley. Immediately the patient was placed on the bed, the waiting medical team moved in to make an early assessment of her condition after her trip from Central London.

Peter and I collected our blankets, placed them loosely on the ambulance trolley, and made our way out of the ward block back to the vehicle where we were joined ten minutes later by Alan.

"Done your LA-4 Peter?" he asked climbing into the back of the ambulance.

"Yes guv," he replied at the same time offering the clipboard for inspection. Alan perused the document for a few minutes, "fine – fine," he said handing the board back to Peter.

"The doctor and nurse will be staying at the hospital for a while, so they won't be travelling back with us, so when your both ready, we will make a move back to our own patch.

"You drive now John – Do you know this part of London?" he asked me.

"Yeah I do," I said as I made myself comfortable behind the steering wheel.

"Good – let's make a move," he said as he took up his position by the internal sliding door to the rear saloon.

Peter contacted Red Base on the R/T, explained the escorts would be staying at the hospital for the time being, where on reply the controller gave a green time and instructed us to RTB.

I pulled our ambulance out of the hospital grounds, turned right in the direction of Wimbledon, and headed *Bloomsbury One* back towards town.

We had reached Clapham Common on this beautiful spring evening when Red Base called requesting our location, after which they asked us too stand by in our present position. A few minutes later the R/T interrupted the small talk going on between the three of us.

Blooms bury One Red Base Over.

Peter picked up the microphone, and with a slight nervousness showing in his voice replied, *Bloomsbury One Over.*

"Thank you Bloomsbury One. Got a call red accident, if your ready for details, over."

"Bloomsbury One Ready, over."

A few seconds passed before the controller continued.

It's A Call Red Accident, second ambulance to a RTA underneath Loughborough Junction Railway Bridge in Coldharbour Lane SE5. Timed to you at 1809 hours, Echo Mike, Bloomsbury One, over."

Peter read the call back to the controller adding his initials as I started the engine, engaged the automatic gearbox, and pulled out into the London bound traffic flow.

"You OK John? – know the way?" Alan asked me as I switched on the blue lights and two tone horns.

"Yes Alan, I know that area very well, spent a lot of time around the Camberwell area when I was a nipper."

"Good, now don't go too mad, read the road ahead, and allow yourself plenty of room to get through the gaps," was the last instruction Alan made during the eight minute journey.

We had reached the Brixton end of Acre Lane when Red Base contacted us again.

"Bloomsbury One, Information for you, over."

The R/T sparked into life.

I turned the two tones off as Peter Picked up the microphone to reply.

"Bloomsbury One, over." Peter said.

The controller continued.

"Bloomsbury One, Brixton Three vehicle has left the scene with a female to Kings College. One male casualty left at scene. Query Purple, over."

"Bloomsbury One, Roger, over." Peter replied before replacing the microphone, and turning to glance at me, which I caught out of the corner of my eye.

Turning the horns on again, we crossed through the stationary traffic at the junction of Brixton High Road and Coldharbour Lane. As the ambulance got nearer the scene, the evening rush hour traffic was at a complete standstill and I found it quite difficult manoeuvring the vehicle towards our target.

It was a chaotic scene that greeted us as I cautiously eased the ambulance between two parked buses that were waiting to be directed to a diversion route that had been set up by the police. At each side of the railway bridge the road had been closed off by police vehicles, making a physical barrier. A large crowd of onlookers had assembled either end of the accident site. Wreckage was everywhere. A motorcycle, minus the front end, was on the pavement under the bridge, the petrol tank with the front forks and a black coloured crash helmet was about twenty yards away.

On the other side of the road, a car with the offside doors and windows smashed stood quite alone in the middle of the road. A few feet from the motorcycle, a bundle covered completely by a red ambulance blanket was obviously our patient. Two police officers joined Alan, Peter and me as we made our way across to the bundle. I felt a bit queasy as we knelt down to remove the blanket to expose the victim. An obvious compound fracture to the left leg was evident with very little blood loss showing on the torn clothing, but the acute position of the head to the body made me swallow my spittle a few times. A very large laceration from scalp to jaw line, again with little blood loss, was the only other physical sign of injury.

"Broken his neck, poor bastard," Alan said, as we all three stood up together. Turning to the policemen he asked, "alright if we move him now, or do you want us to wait a bit?"

"Just give us a ten more minutes to finish taking some measurements, plus a couple of photos, and then his all yours," the senior officer of the two replied."

"What happened to the driver of the car?" I asked nodding towards the damaged saloon.

"Oh, he's sitting in the police van over there," he said pointing, "not a mark on him. Didn't want to go to hospital with the other ambulance crew when they asked him."

"Check him out Peter," Alan said interrupting the young officer.

As Peter made his way across to the police van, Alan and I unloaded the trolley bed along with the scoop stretcher and rubber sheet and prepared the equipment ready to use immediately the police gave permission for the removal of the casualty. Looking around the scene, I saw police officers taking measurements everywhere, including the distances between different bits of the scattered debris. A fire tender had arrived and the crew began washing down the spillage from the ruptured petrol tank and sweeping up the glass fragments that covered the road. Peter joined us as we were still waiting to carry out the removal.

"Driver's ok, just wants to get home, he's not hurt at all," he said, with relief in his voice.

In front of the large crowd of onlookers that had assembled, boosted in numbers by the arrival of trains every few minutes at the nearby station, Peter and I used the scoop stretcher to lift the young rider onto the trolley bed as Alan covered him with the blanket. Within a minute he was loaded onto the ambulance. With Alan sitting alongside me in the cab and Peter with a policeman in the rear, I slowly moved *Bloomsbury One* away from the accident scene towards Denmark Hill.

"No lights or horns John, nice and easy – do you know where King's is?"

"Yes, off Denmark Hill."

"That's right," Alan said as he lifted the microphone.

"Bloomsbury One, Red Base Over."

"Bloomsbury One."

"Yeah, Bloomsbury One, we are mobile from scene, Purple One, can you advise Kings that we would like to be met outside casualty by a doctor in about five minutes, over."

The controller replied.

"King's, five minutes, Roger Bloomsbury One, over."

Within the five reported minutes I had pulled into the ambulance bay outside King's College casualty, where a waiting doctor with stethoscope in hand along with a casualty sister opened the rear door enough to gain entry too join my colleague and the policeman in the rear saloon.

I turned in my seat to watch the procedure carried out by the doctor as he examined our casualty from head to toe, turning afterwards to his audience stating the obvious injuries that were evident, and glancing at his watch, gave a time of death as 1852 hours for the records.

After the doctor and sister had returned to their department, Alan directed me around to the rear of the hospital, where well-hidden doors led to the Purple Annex. Alan and the police officer followed Peter and me as we entered the mortuary with our patient. We were met half way along a cold corridor by a white-coated porter.

"Hello lads, this way," he said pointing and leading the way, which led to the fridge room where we lifted our biker onto a detachable metal tray that was resting on a wheeled trolley. Here the police officer and porter undressed the victim, taking note of personal possessions which might reveal the identity of the unfortunate male.

Holding up a well-thumbed driving licence the officer said, "If the licence is his, then his name is James Julian Johnson, date of birth is 03-06-1950, but I can't confirm it until he has been formally identified, so I'll let your control know later for your records," the officer said.

Placing the clothing and personal belongings into separate plastic bags the porter then attached the necessary labels, after which he attached another label to the victim's right toe, which I noted, *Unknown Male – RTA – in at 1900 hours – 4th May 1975.*

After covering the body in a white sheet, we helped the porter slide the tray from the trolley into a vacant shelf in the large accommodating fridge.

Outside it was nice to get back to the fresh air and feel the warmth from the last rays from the day's sunshine. Back at casualty, we cleaned up the equipment and I was mopping the floor of the ambulance when Peter came out to tell me a cup of tea was to be had in the staff room. That tea, along with a cigarette, was a real treat after the last couple of hours. I shivered as I thought to myself, *Iv'e actually driven on my first accident call through rush hour traffic, seen and moved a road accident fatality, been in a mortuary, which I was dreading after the training trip to Guys'.*

My daydreaming was broken as Alan entered the room to claim his cup of tea.

"Alright boys? – the ambulance clean and ready to go?" he asked.

"Yes," Peter said, continuing, "what do I do about the patients name etc."

"Control will let us know when the name has been confirmed, but for now, just put down on your LA-4, an unknown male, approx age twenty five, that's about all you can put down apart from the obvious injury and the number of the police officer who came with the ambulance. Oh, another thing, the female patient that the Brixton vehicle bought in is now in theatre. She's got a fractured pelvis and serious internal injuries. Only seventeen years old. The copper told me that witnesses said the bike was doing about sixty miles an hour along Coldharbour Lane on the wrong side of the road when he braked and skidded, glanced off the side of the car, and went headlong into the brickwork under the railway bridge. He said, people thought it was a bomb that had gone off, by the sound it made. Silly little bastard – what a waste!"

We sat there in silence, each enjoying another cigarette, before Alan said we should think about making a move back. The return journey took in a vehicle refuel at headquarters before crossing the Thames and on to Bloomsbury.

Back on station after replacing the dirty blankets on the ambulance, Red Base put us on half an hour meal break. The talk in the mess room obviously revolved around the afternoon's events and when number three crew joined us for a cuppa they were all ears as Alan went into graphic details of the RTA.

The conversation was cut short as the emergency line burst into life – ear shattering in the very small room. Peter, who was sitting nearest the phone, took down the details of the call being transmitted from headquarters, then passed the endorsed LA-4 form across to the other crew who were already on their feet ready to go.

"What you got mate?" Alan asked as they started for the door.

"Collapse in Oxford Street, near Woolworths, see ye'r later," was the reply as the crew left the room, and a few seconds later the engine was fired on *Bloomsbury Three*, followed by the sound of the two tones as it made it's way out into Russell Square.

Our meal-break was cut short by ten minutes when the bells went off again; this time it was I who answered the red phone.

"Call Red Accident For You Bloomsbury," said the voice on the other end, as I put the receiver to my ear.

With pen poised I replied, "Go Ahead."

"It's a call to Caledonian Road Railway Station, Caledonian Road N1. Female fallen down a staircase, arm injury, timed to you at 2015 hours, Romeo Uniform."

I read the call back to the controller, ending with my initials, saying that Bloomsbury One crew were coming off meal break to attend. I handed the LA-4 to Peter as Alan looked over his shoulder to read the call received.

"You drive John," he said as we made our way to the garage to board our ambulance.

With a beautiful sunset settling over the rooftops, I steered *Bloomsbury One* north towards Kings Cross and Caledonian Road with the two tones blaring and the blue lights flashing. The journey was a lot easier and faster than the run earlier that day. The traffic, although heavy, was flowing quite freely, allowing room for the ambulance to pass at an even speed throughout the five minute run.

We found our patient being looked after by a couple of railway personnel at the ticket office, just inside the station entrance. The sixty four year old lady had tripped over the last few steps coming down the long staircase from the platforms above and put her arm out to break the fall, which resulted in a fracture to her right wrist. After immobilising her arm with an inflatable splint and insuring she had not injured herself anywhere else, we used the carrying chair, much to her disapproval, to move her with her luggage to the waiting ambulance. After loading, we made a normal traffic journey again north along the Caledonian Road towards Holloway.

Alan, who was sitting up front with me in the cab, directed me to the entrance of the casualty department for the Royal Northern Hospital which was situated in Holloway High Road.

With the procedures carried out after unloading our patient into the department, Peter obtained a green time from control over the R/T, and we headed once again to base.

We received one more call from station on that second day at Bloomsbury, which turned out to be a hoax, also attended by the other two emergency services. Someone had dialled the treble nines and reported a kitchen fire in a restaurant at Wardour Street in the middle of Soho, home to the theatres, clubs and the red light district of central London. Arriving at the scene we were met by a mass of flashing blue lights and noise from the two tones as the other emergency vehicles struggled with the traffic and pedestrians in the narrow streets of this part of town. After a quick assessment of the situation by the fire and police officers, all three services were stood down and returned to their stations.

My trip home to South London after my shift had finished on that second day at Bloomsbury as an ambulance-man is something that will live with me forever: I had found a good friend in my crew-mate Peter; I had achieved what I had set out to do back in February; and for once in my life I felt a sense of purpose. I was part of a very big team with the job of looking out for the well-being of others, and not just 'looking after number one'.

The following weeks at Bloomsbury saw us fall into a routine of station, vehicle and equipment cleaning, question and answer periods with Alan, and many call-outs. All the time we were gaining in confidence, and with each call-out we learnt something new. My emergency driving also became second nature to me, as I quickly learnt to read the road and surface conditions, a real benefit, not only to myself but also to my colleague, who could be working on a restless casualty in the back.

Over these weeks, Alan was still making his daily notes on the progress of Peter and I. As time went on, Alan kept more in the background when we attended or treated casualties, only making himself available if extra equipment was required from the ambulance or, as in one case, assistance was needed in a procedure we hadn't tried 'in the field' as yet.

A case in point was our first resuscitation attempt after a call to a collapse in a seedy nightclub in the back streets of Soho. We were on our fourth night duty turn at Bloomsbury when the call came in, requesting our attendance to the club at a few minutes to midnight.

I was the attendant on that shift and on our arrival at the club we were directed down a very narrow and dark staircase to a basement where in the secluded lighting was a small bottle-filled bar, surrounded by high stools. At the centre of the room was a raised platform, where a naked young woman gyrated to a very loud Beatles number. Around this stage, sitting open-mouthed was a small, mostly male audience, amongst whom was an elderly gentleman who was leaning over to one side as if asleep. In fact, he had vomited down his three piece suit and on examination we discovered him to be unconscious.

Some of the patrons were quite indignant as we asked for some room to move our patient to the carrying chair. During this manoeuvre, I lost the carotid pulse that I was monitoring, so we quickly placed the man on the floor to start resuscitation. Alan shouted out to the barman for the lighting to be put on as he raced up the staircase to get the aspirator and oxygen equipment from the ambulance. The music stopped almost at once as the lower floor was bathed in fluorescent light. I started to use the 'Brook's' airway for the first time as Peter started the closed chest cardiac massage. A few oohs and aahs were heard from the visitors as they backed away to the bar area.

Alan arrived back in no time at all and after aspirating the airway and attaching the oxygen line to the resui-bag we continued the full resuscitation procedure for the next ten minutes, when Alan suggested we make a move upstairs as quickly as possible to the ambulance.

In less than three minutes we had our patient onboard Bloomsbury One. A burley club bouncer had followed us up the staircase to the street level with the first aid satchel, oxygen bottle, and the aspirator, which saved us a lot of time. Peter and I continued working on the old chap in the rear of the ambulance as Alan closed the doors and slid behind the steering wheel, placed a blue call with Red Base, and with horns blaring, he headed for the casualty at the Middlesex Hospital.

In the crash room, the medical team worked on our elderly patient for nearly forty minutes before the doctor leading the team called a halt, stating they had gone far enough, and there was no more that they could do for the poor old chap.

Outside in the ambulance after we had cleaned up, Alan said he was pleased with the way we had dealt with the job under the conditions that faced us all back at the club.

"You will find that in most cases like the one tonight, you will be on your own, not many members of the public like to get involved, although they all like standing there watching you go about your business, reason being, most people don't know what to do in the circumstances, probably like ourselves before coming into this job."

It was a warm but damp day that was to be Alan's last as Instructor to Peter and myself on *Bloomsbury One*. His departure, without warning, came as a surprise to the pair of us, halfway through a busy early-turn shift. The three of us were travelling back to station after our forth call of the morning when control yet again requested over the R/T our state and position.

"Bloomsbury One Report, Red Base, over."

"Bloomsbury One, Green at Kingsway approaching Holborn Underground Station."

"Thank you Bloomsbury One. Got a Call Red accident if you're ready for details, over."

"Roger, go ahead."

"It's a Call Red RTA to the Piccadilly Underpass, Eastbound, W1, timed to you at 1103 Hours Delta Foxtrot, Red Base Over."

I read the call back to Delta Foxtrot, adding my initials, as Peter turned the ambulance into Long Acre near Bow Street courts and headed in the direction of Covent Garden. With the 'blues and twos' running, we crossed Leicester Square through into Piccadilly Circus and on to the Piccadilly thoroughfare leading to the underpass. Although the ground was wet, the clouds had parted allowing brilliant sunshine to bathe the scene as we arrived.

Road works were being carried out on the Westbound carriageway, where a barrier had been erected for the protection of the road gang. One of the workers had jumped the barrier and had run across the road to the North side of the underpass where he had been struck by a car doing thirty five miles an hour coming out of the underpass tunnel in the Eastbound direction.

A very large crowd had gathered at the side of the road to witness our arrival.

As the police had stopped all the traffic in both directions, Peter had plenty of room to park the ambulance beside the spread-eagled workman lying face-down in the centre of the carriageway.

On examination, his injuries were horrific. He was unconscious, with serious wounds to his skull. Both legs and one arm were obviously fractured and massive blood loss was evident on the torn dirty clothing.

"The driver of the car is alright – where are you going with this one?" A young-looking policeman asked, bending down beside me.

"St George's," I said, without looking up.

"Bit of a mess, aint he!" the policeman said standing up and moving away.

"Yeah, just a bit," I answered, as Peter arrived at my side.

After aspirating and inserting an airway, we immediately used the scoop stretcher to move our patient across to the rubber-sheeted trolley bed prepared by Alan and then forward onto the ambulance, where we made attempts to cover the open wound sites and with pressure dressings to try and stem the blood flow from a large laceration to his abdomen.

Whilst all this action was happening in the back of the ambulance, Alan had placed a blue call with Red base over the R/T, stating we would be mobile with a male patient with multiple injuries, and unconscious, we would be running to the casualty at St Georges Hospital at Hyde Park Corner with an ETA of six minutes.

"Get going to St George's when your ready," Alan said, as he jumped down from the ambulance and closed the rear doors behind him.

"Let's go Pete – let's get him in quick," I said, after Alan's departure.

Peter slid into the drivers seat and selected the auto-gearbox to allow the vehicle to move away from the scene.

"What about Alan?" he asked without turning around.

"We can't wait, this bloke's in a bad way," I replied, looking down at the young blood-covered male. We left the scene with two-tones and blue lights running and Peter somehow found a path through the congested traffic around Hyde Park Corner – made worse by the closure of the underpass

– and just three minutes later slowly eased *Bloomsbury One* into the ambulance reception bay under the arch outside St Georges Hospital casualty department. With help in the crash room, we moved the patient across to the waiting trolley where Peter and I unhooked the scoop stretcher, and slid it away from beneath the young man, leaving him in exactly the same position as he had been in the roadway.

"Oh dear!" a grey haired doctor stated as he lifted the dressing away from the head injury, "We've got serious lacerations to the cerebrum, also we've got bone embedded in the base," he continued, bending down to take a closer look.

Peter and I went outside to clean ourselves as well as the equipment, which was in a dreadful state. The blankets were placed to one side and the rubber sheet put into a plastic bag ready to be cleaned on our return to station. Peter had bloodstains on the front of his shirt and I had stains on my trousers where I had knelt down to examine the casualty on our arrival at the accident site. I was sitting on a seat outside the casualty department filling out the emergency LA-4 form and smoking a cigarette when Alan appeared out of the swing doors and walked towards me.

"Where's Peter?" he asked, lighting one of his own cigarettes.

"Taking the mop and bucket back after cleaning the back out," I replied, without looking up from my writing. He took a seat beside me without saying a word, but looked across to see what I had written on the LA-4. Peter joined us after a couple of minutes. He turned to Alan and asked, "How did you get back here guv? – I thought we would have to go back to the underpass for you."

"Got a lift in a police car when they finished measuring up at the scene. The road's back open now, but it caused a traffic jam right back to Knights bridge and Victoria. It will take a couple of hours to sort itself out, they tell me."

"How you doing?" he said turning back to me.

"Finished," I said, offering my paperwork on the clipboard for him to inspect.

"Fine," Alan said, standing up and handing the board back to me, "let's just whip back into the re-sus room and see how they are getting on before we go."

He led the way back through the swing doors. In the resuscitation room, two doctors were standing talking as the nursing staff were in the process of cleaning up the area. The patient was lying on his back, covered completely by a blue hospital blanket.

"Hello lads," the grey-haired doctor said, turning to greet us as we entered the room. "Your young man unfortunately had massive injuries, so much so that he died a few minutes ago... Come across and have a look." He led us towards the covered body. Slowly removing the blanket to reveal the now naked body, he continued, "Terrible head injuries," pointing to the two fracture sites. "I think he must have left half his brains on the road. I'm quite surprised he survived as long as he did, massive internal injuries as well," he said nodding towards the victim's open abdominal wound. "The legs, although a mess, we could have done something about … well there we are." He pulled the blanket back over the body. "Thanks for what you've done," he said smiling, "but we were on a loser, I think, from the moment this poor chap was knocked down."

He turned back to join his colleague on the other side of the room.

Walking back along the corridor towards the exit, Alan stopped and turned to the pair of us.

"Well boy's, you'll be on your own from now on. You've both done very well, so keep it up, but don't forget, you've still got a lot to learn, so take your time and think before you rush into anything. It's been very pleasant working with the pair of you over the last few weeks and you have been a credit to your instructors back at training school – all I can say now is well done and good luck!"

With that, Alan turned and walked back down the corridor towards the casualty reception area where he had arranged to be met and transported back to Waterloo headquarters.

Peter and I climbed aboard the ambulance, looked at each other and let out a loud yelp.

"On our own, I don't believe it!" I said.

"Unbelievable!" Peter said with a broad grin.

"Oh well… here we go," I said, as I lifted the microphone from its holder.

"Red Base – Bloomsbury One – Red Base – Over."

"Bloomsbury One – Over."

"Yes, Bloomsbury One – Green At St Georges Hyde Park Corner – Request RTB To Clean Up And Uniform Change – Over."

"Roger Bloomsbury One – Green Time of 1210 Hours – Return To Base – Over."

"Bloomsbury One – Roger – Over."

"Thank You Bloomsbury – Red Base Out."

I replaced the microphone as Peter fired the engine and moved the ambulance out to join the traffic at Hyde Park Corner, still heavily congested with vehicles held up by the accident an hour earlier. Our return to station saw the number three ambulance disappearing into the distance on a call with lights flashing and the two tones blaring, as it headed off in the direction of the West End.

It felt strange being on station without a training officer present, looking over our shoulders, giving orders or asking questions. After replacing the soiled blankets on the vehicle and cleaning the rubber sheet and scoop stretcher, we both changed into fresh uniforms, placing the soiled ones in a basket that would be picked up later by the headquarters service van.

Sitting in the mess room with a cup of tea and a cigarette after advising control we were ready for the road gave the pair of us time to reflect on the morning's events and to gather our thoughts now we were truly on our own as an ambulance crew. Forty minutes before we were due to be relieved by the late turn crew, we turned out to a call for the first time alone. It was to a very up-market block of flats at

Park Road near Baker Street station, overlooking the massive Regents Park Gardens.

An elderly lady who was visiting her son's apartment had collapsed with chest pains which left her short of breath and in a state of panic. On our arrival at the third floor we were met by a well-dressed middle-aged man who led us through to a large lounge furnished in a style you might see in the well-to-do magazines you flip through whilst waiting your turn in dentist's or doctor's surgeries. The floor was covered in a very deep pile carpet and various eastern finished rugs complemented the fine décor. Our patient, smelling of lavender water, was sitting upright on a brown leather chesterfield sofa, looking quite apologetic that we had been troubled.

"Have you still got chest pains?" I said, kneeling down by the couch and taking her wrist to find the pulse.

"A little," she replied weakly.

"How long has the young lady been like this?" I turned to ask the gentleman.

"About half an hour now. My mother only arrived a short while ago after travelling up from the South coast to visit me," he replied anxiously.

While the crosstalk was going on, Peter had returned to the ambulance to collect the carrying chair, another blanket, and the oxygen bottle.

"Has your mother any medical condition that you know of?" I asked the son.

"None. Never had a days illness in her seventy four years," he said, leaning across to brush a hair away from his mother's sweating but cold forehead.

Peter arrived back in the room. We administered the oxygen straight away as the cyanosis was more evident than when we first arrived. We slowly moved the lady to the carrying chair and after covering her in the blankets had to lift the chair across the carpeted area to the hallway due to the depth of carpet pile. The son followed behind with the oxygen bottle under his arm allowing enough slack for the tubing from the cylinder valve to the facemask his mother was wearing. After a fast lift ride to the ground floor, we loaded our patient into the vehicle and on to the trolley bed in an upright position. Peter gave us a steady ride along the Marylebone Road into Great Portland Street and around to the casualty department of the Middlesex Hospital.

Wheeling the lady into the department, we were met by a staff nurse who approached us from the reception area.

"What have we here then?" she asked joyfully, first glancing at the elderly lady then myself.

"Chest pains," I said, at the same time nodding towards the resuscitation room doors.

"Right, we're just going to pop you in here so the doctor can have a look at you," the young staff nurse said, pushing the doors open for us to enter.

"If you go to the reception desk and book the lady in, then I'll pop out to see you in a minute," she said to the worried-looking son, who was attempting to follow us into the crash room.

"Chest pains, no history, cyanosed when we got there," I said to the casualty sister, who had joined us as Peter and I were lifting the frail lady onto the hospital trolley. After swapping the oxygen over to the hospital supply, Peter removed our trolley, blankets and oxygen cylinder to the corridor. Returning to the resuscitation room after I had finished the paperwork, the sister informed us that the elderly lady had suffered a heart attack and would shortly be moved to the coronary care unit. She looked quite frail and unwell lying on the trolley, hooked up to various monitors and intravenous lines. Before leaving the room I walked across to the trolley, took the old lady by the hand and with a slight squeeze whished her all the best. Opening her eyes slowly, she just smiled her reply.

On our return to station, Peter was just reversing the ambulance into the garage when the emergency alarm bells started ringing. A few seconds later, our relief crew and their instructor were aboard *Bloomsbury One* and on their way to the first call of their shift.

I joined my wife for a cup of tea on my return home to Mitcham after dropping Peter off in nearby Norbury at the end of a slow homeward journey across London to the southern suburbs.

"How did it go?" she asked, taking a seat alongside me on the couch. Without going into the graphic details, I gave her a rundown of the morning's events, ending by saying that Alan our instructor had left Peter and I at St Georges Hospital, stating we were ready to be left alone to work as a crew and that we were apprehensive but very pleased.

Our first week of unsupervised night duty at Bloomsbury turned out to be a very busy period for us with frequent runs to Soho and the West End for collapse calls, usually drink related or one of our regular overdose patients who we would recognized immediately on arrival at the scene. Most were removed to the ever-busy Middlesex casualty department, which at times looked like a battlefield, with aggressive blood soaked youths demanding treatment from the overworked casualty staff. Most of the time the crash room areas were occupied by overdose patients having their stomachs washed out or awaiting their turn to be removed to the recovery wards by the blue-coated porters.

One of the overdose calls we received was to a dark alleyway behind Piccadilly Circus, away from the prying eyes of theatregoers and foreign tourists, where we found a young male lying on his back between a couple of dustbins. Two probationary police officers along with their sergeant on foot patrol arrived just as we started our examination of the youth.

"What we got mate?" the sergeant asked shining his torch over my shoulder.

"Unconscious male, addict I think – I haven't seen him before," I replied without turning around.

A syringe was still embedded beneath the skin in our patient's left forearm, a thin leather strap obviously used as a tourniquet was lying across his dirty damp shirt. After aspirating the vomit and inserting an airway we moved our patient with the help of one of the officers across to the trolley bed.

"What hospital you going to?" I heard the sergeant ask Peter as I attached the oxygen mask to the still unconscious male, who we had now moved to the well lit rear saloon of the ambulance.

"From here, Westminster casualty, it's the nearest," Peter said as he climbed into the cab and fired the engine.

"Alright if one of my lads comes along with you?" the sergeant asked, holding onto the door handle.

"Yeah fine, jump up alongside me in the cab," Peter said, as he engaged the gears, ready to pull away. With the policeman onboard, as the ambulance started to move, I heard Peter place a blue call to Red Base.

"Priority."

"Go Ahead Priority."

"Bloomsbury One, Blue to Westminster, Young Male Unconscious, ETA, Five Minutes, Over."

The controller read the request back as Peter switched on the blue lights, and dabbed the two tone switch to warn others of our movement in the still busy West End streets.

At the Westminster Hospital our patient was quickly conveyed to the resuscitation room where he was met by the pre-warned crash team. With the transfer to the hospital trolley, the youth was quickly undressed, and the standard procedures carried out by the waiting team started, which over the past few weeks I had learnt varies very little from one casualty unit to another.

The policeman searched the discarded clothing for some form of identification for the young man, finding only a second class railway ticket to London from Newcastle, along with a telephone number scribbled on a torn piece of paper and a few coppers in loose change.

I learnt the following night, when we arrived back at Westminster casualty with another patient, that the male we had brought in the previous night had died in re-sus as a result of a massive overdose of heroin. He was just sixteen years of age. He had been living rough in the Charing Cross area of London after running away from home in Newcastle three weeks earlier.

Our first week of unsupervised night duty came to an end after a complete shift spent away from station, with six calls following one after another. The first to a road traffic at Oxford Circus, where we conveyed two casualties with superficial head wounds to the Middlesex casualty The second was for a removal by doctors request of an elderly gentleman suffering with respiratory distress to St Thomas Hospital, this removal was made all the worse by the fact that he lived on the seventh floor of a block of flats, with the lift out of order due to vandalism.

We struggled down the concrete staircase with our fifteen-stone patient, an oxygen bottle balanced precariously across his lap as we made the decent. Making our return to base from St Thomas's, we received the third call of the night on the R/T as we approached Russell Square, just a few yards from station. It was to Kings Cross Railway Station, where an attendant on a night sleeper train had scalded his hands with boiling water in the kitchen buffet carriage. On our arrival we were told that a hot water urn had tipped over as he was attempting to slide it across a worktop unit, resulting in second degree burns to both hands. We ran cold water from the buffet supply over his hands for several minutes before attempting to remove two heavy gold rings from his fingers, that were being compressed by the resulting swelling. After the successful removal of the rings, we covered the hands in cold wet dressings, and with a little use of the pain relief gas Enternox, we made our departure from the railway station, and conveyed our patient to the University College Hospital.

Our fourth call was received as I was pulling the ambulance out of the hospital grounds into Gower Street. Red Base gave us a call to Tottenham Court Road near Goodge Street underground station, where the police were in attendance with a male that had several stab wounds. With the traffic a lot lighter now that most late night revellers had returned home, I turned *Bloomsbury One* into Tottenham Court Road and arrived at scene after just a couple of minutes running time.

The victim, a twenty-year-old male, was surrounded by a dozen police officers as Peter and I eased our way through to our patient. He was standing up, supported on one side by an inspector. Peter suggested that we walk him to the ambulance where we could make a better assessment of his injuries.

The worse for drink, our casualty was very abusive towards us and the two policeman that had joined us in the rear of the ambulance to witness the examination. He had three deep lacerations to his right forearm, one penetrating wound to his right thigh and another penetrating wound to his right shoulder. His left eye was closing fast with a large contusion obviously caused by a closed fist.

The youth refused all attempts by Peter and I to dress his wounds or to make any further examinations for injury sites. With the Middlesex Hospital just around the corner, we decided to make a move, and with the two police officers on board to assist Peter in keeping the patient still, I pulled the ambulance away from the scene and forwards to the hospital. Again, with the help of the officers, we had to manhandle the youth into a side room (kept for these situations) so he could be examined by the medical staff with the assistance of the police.

It took me a little while to clean the rear saloon of the ambulance of the blood that the youth had deposited whilst throwing his arms around during the short journey.

"Want a quick cuppa John?" Peter asked me as he joined me at the back of the ambulance.

"Love one," I replied as I switched off the saloon lighting and closed the rear doors.

We were told over tea in the staff room by the staff nurse that our patient had to be sedated before the doctor could make any form of examination or treatment. It seems that you just can't help some people.

After climbing into the cab beside me, Peter removed the microphone to contact Red Base.

"Red Base, Bloomsbury One – Red Base – Over."

"Bloomsbury One – Over."

"Bloomsbury One – Green at the Middlesex – Over."

"Thank you Bloomsbury One – Green Time of 0247 hours – I have a Call Red accident for you if you're ready for details – Over."

"Yes, Go Ahead – Over," Peter replied, with pen ready to take the details down.

"It's a Call Red accident to a house fire with persons reported trapped, at number seventeen, Churchill Gardens Estate, Churchill Gardens Road West One. Westminster One is already running to scene, call timed to you at 0248 hours, and report on arrival, my initials are Echo Delta, Bloomsbury One – Over.

Peter read the call back as I picked up the road atlas to pinpoint the given location that was well off our regular patch. I started the engine and moved *Bloomsbury One* south towards our call, switching on the blue lights we crossed Oxford Street, and on towards Charing Cross and Whitehall, using the horns only as we approached Parliament Square where a build up of traffic had occurred. We carried on to the Millbank leading us into Grosvenor Road where we followed another ambulance that had come in from our left across Vauxhall Bridge. Arriving at the incident, we were met by a blaze of blue lights, a strong smell of smoke hit us as we climbed down from the ambulance after reporting our arrival time to Red Base. An ambulance officer approached us as a ambulance was pulling away from the scene with it's blue lights running.

"Bloomsbury crew?" he inquired.

"Yes sir" Peter replied.

"See that ambulance over there," he said pointing to his right. Before waiting for a reply he continued, "Park up behind that vehicle, it's Oval One, and wait there to you hear from me."

He walked away towards a white helmeted fire officer. The Oval crew walked up to join us beside our vehicle. After informal greetings Peter asked, "What's going on – do you know?"

The older of the two replied, "All we know is that Westminster One removed a woman who was running up and down the street with her nightdress alight, but the gov'nor thinks there's another two people in there." He nodded towards the burning building fifty yards away.

Fireman were running everywhere, more hoses were being run alongside the dozen that were already fully charged. Two turntable ladders were in use, with fireman aloft, almost lost to sight due the mixture of smoke and steam being emitted from the building. The Oval crew were called forward by the ambulance officer to transport a child that the fireman, wearing breathing equipment, had just removed from the lower floor of the blackened building. Another ambulance pulled in behind ours a few minutes later, but before we could make ourselves known to the new arrivals the officer waved us forward to where he was standing. Our patient was being carried down one of the turntable ladders over the shoulder of a black-faced fireman. The casualty was lowered by helping hands on to our prepared trolley bed.

"Into the ambulance and we'll have a look at him," the officer ordered, leading the way.

Under the bright lighting in the rear of the ambulance we could see the full extent of the injuries this unfortunate male had received. He was unconscious. His body was burnt black and was still smouldering and hot to touch. All the body hair, apart from a little around the crutch area, had been burnt away, as had any clothing that he had been wearing. With an airway inserted, I asked a policeman who had boarded the ambulance to hold the oxygen mask over the patient's face whilst the ambulance officer, Peter and I soaked burn sheets in water before placing them as best we could over the casualty.

"Right – make your way to Westminster casualty with him, I'll let them know you are on the way." Looking around he continued, "the police officer will be staying with you."

With that, he jumped down from the back, closed the doors and shouted, "Off you go!"

I slid behind the steering wheel, and with an "OK" from Peter I eased *Bloomsbury One* slowly across the charged fire hoses, and away from the tragic scene. A couple of minutes later and again with willing hands, we unloaded our patient into the crash room area of the casualty department, where another medical team was treating the female that the Westminster One ambulance had conveyed. As I cleaned the ambulance saloon whilst Peter was doing the paperwork, the one thing I couldn't disguise, with either disinfectant or fresh air spray, was the burning smell. It's an aroma that one never forgets. Walking back into the unit after doing the cleaning I met up with Peter in the reception area.

"I've just been on to Red Base on the land line. The woman the Westminster crew bought in is going to be transferred to the burns unit at Roehampton and if the delay here is not too long, they want us to do it – so we've time for a very quick cuppa."

He led the way to the staff room where we quickly settled down with a warm drink and a cigarette, only to be interrupted by a staff nurse who poked her head round the door to inform us that they would be ready to move in ten minutes time. We swallowed the tea down and after extinguishing our cigarettes made our way back to the ambulance to collect our trolley bed with a couple of clean blankets. The patient was covered from head to toe in white sheeting, with just a portion cut away to expose the face, which was a mixture of colours between bright pink at the forehead to black around the mouth and chin. She was conscious, but obviously heavily sedated, as her eyes lazily surveyed the busy scene going on around her. With help from the casualty staff, we moved the woman on the ambulance trolley away from the crash room, along the corridor with two nurses holding aloft two drip lines that were attached to the patient, through the swing doors, and out to our waiting ambulance.

"You the driver?" a middle aged doctor with a pair of bifocals resting at a perilous angle on the end of his nose asked me as I was closing the rear doors.

"Yes," I said, waiting for the next question.

"Quick as you can, if you would please," he said turning to join his colleagues in the rear saloon as I continued to close the doors.

Peter advised Red Base over the R/T that we were mobile to Roehampton as I headed towards Lambeth Bridge, the Albert Embankment and the A3036 road that would take us through South London to the A3 and Putney Heath. I made good time with blue lights flashing, and only once having to use the horns as we got to the one way system at Wandsworth High Street, where a build up of early morning market traffic heading for central London was heavy in the narrow high street. Because we had onboard two doctors and a nurse as escorts to the patient, Peter had joined me up front, and helped in directing me as we got nearer our destination at Roehampton Lane. After a seventeen-minute run from Central London, I pulled *Bloomsbury One* into the entrance of Queen Mary's Hospital and followed the signs that led me to the rear of the buildings and the burns unit, where a reception party consisting of several people was waiting in the warm early morning air for our arrival. Peter and I went as far as the sterile area inside the unit with our patient, before we handed over to two white-gowned porters who continued along the corridor with the escorts to the prepared room for the incoming female.

It was the first time either of us had been inside a burns unit, and whilst waiting in the long corridor, we could see through the large glass partitions that separated the cubicles, several badly burned patients suspended on hammock type supports, or lying on larger than usual type beds surrounded by electric fans cooling the air around them.

A beautiful dawn was breaking across the rooftops as the two doctors and the escort nurse joined Peter and myself outside the unit ready for the return journey to Westminster.

On our return at long last to our station, after dropping the escorts off at the Westminster Hospital, Peter and I set about cleaning the inside of the ambulance with a strong solution of disinfectant to try and mask the strong smell of burning that still lingered. The trolley bed was remade with fresh blankets and the first aid satchel re-stocked.

"Good morning lads," a young looking training officer said as he entered the mess room where Peter and I were enjoying a cup of tea before going off duty.

"Morning gov," we both replied together.

"Tea?" I asked, getting up.

"Please," he said, as he removed his uniform jacket and placed it on the row of hooks behind the door. Taking a seat at the table where I had placed his mug of tea he asked.

"Busy night? By the smell of your clothes you've been on a fire job."

"Yeah, has been busy, been out all night," Peter said, continuing with a brief rundown of the nights events, ending with the fire call to Pimlico, and the transfer run to the burns unit.

During the conversation, the early turn crew arrived together on station, ready to join their instructor and take over *Bloomsbury One* from myself and Peter.

"What's she like for juice?" the officer asked as we were getting ready to go off duty.

"Needs filling up," I said, turning to face the two nervous-looking crew members who were looking at the massive wall map that displayed Bloomsbury's catchment area. Bidding our farewells, we left the station and very shortly had joined the morning rush hour traffic on our southbound journey home.

Over breakfast, my wife and I settled down to watch the television local news, the main story being the Pimlico fire, where we were informed that four casualties had been removed from the scene, one of whom was still being treated at Westminster Hospital. Another, a female, had been transferred to a burns unit during the early hours. The other two, a teenage girl, and an elderly woman, had been rescued from the premises by firemen, but had been certified dead on arrival at hospital. The newscaster continued to say that police investigations were still ongoing as regards the cause of the fire, but early findings pointed to an electrical fault in the ground floor kitchen as being a possible cause.

After a long soak in the bath to try and loose the burning smell that seemed to be clinging to me, I rolled into bed, knowing I had two full days off duty before returning to start a late-turn week on the following Friday. Sleep came to me very slowly, as I struggled to erase the events of the past night from my thoughts.

On the Thursday morning I received a call at home from Peter saying he would not be reporting for duty for the following week, due to the death of his mother-in-law, and that he had advised the training section at headquarters of the situation, and would telephone me when he was available for duty.

I left home earlier than usual on the Friday afternoon to make my way to Bloomsbury in time to see if I would have to report anywhere else, due to my crewmate not being available for duty for the forthcoming week. Both Bloomsbury vehicles were out when I arrived on station, so after making myself a coffee, I contacted the training office at headquarters on the landline, and explained the situation. I was put through to a training officer who was aware that my colleague had a family bereavement, and that relief cover had been arranged to cover Peter's duty turns over the following seven days.

Sitting alone in the mess room, sipping another cup of coffee, and enjoying a cigarette whilst watching the wall clock hands move closer to my duty time, I heard the mess room door slowly open behind me.

"Hello mate!" came in a quite voice from a young blond haired uniformed man as he entered the room.

"Hi," I said turning to face him.

Nervously as he crossed the room he announced that he had been sent to Bloomsbury to cover for a week of late turn, due to somebody going sick.

"Not sick, it's my mate you're covering. He's had a death in the family, so he will be off for about a week so I've been told.

"Coffee?" I asked him, holding a cup in the air.

"Ta, love one," he said sliding a chair forward to sit at the table.

"Name's John," I said as I placed his mug of coffee on the table.

"David," he replied, offering his hand to shake.

Returning to my chair and drink, I asked him if he had worked at Bloomsbury before.

"No, not at all, I've only been out of training school since last Friday, done two shifts at Smithfield and two at head-quarters on *Quebec Three*."

'Fuck me,' I thought to myself.

The small-talk continued until well past the changeover time of three o'clock, when I heard an Ambulance backing into the garage, *Bloomsbury One* was back on station.

David and I carried out the vehicle check, where the first aid satchel was replenished with several dressings, the oxygen cylinder changed due to a low reading, and a couple of dirty blankets replaced, everything else was in order. After washing the rear saloon floor, we both checked the oil and fuel levels, and did a quick tidy up of the front cab.

"Do you want to drive or attend?" I asked David on our return to the mess room.

Clearing his throat he answered, "I don't know the area very well – Will it be alright if I attend?"

"Yes, fine," I said, handing him the clipboard for our vehicle.

"Have you been here long John?"

"Coming on six weeks now, couple of weeks unsupervised, just getting used to working on our own."

"Still get nervous?" he asked, watching for my reaction.

Laughing aloud I answered, "Every time that bloody red phone rings, I shit myself." Getting up and making my way to the door, I said, "Come on Dave, let's clean the ambulance, it's a bit grubby on the outside – shouldn't take the pair of us too long."

I led him out to the garage area. With long brushes we soaped *Bloomsbury One* from top to bottom, followed by rinsing, using one of the pressure hoses pulled out from the wall reels. We had just finished sweeping the standing water out of the garage, when the alarm repeater bells sprang into life on the wall behind us.

The call was to a doctor's surgery at Richmond Avenue in the Barnsbury area of North London, a couple of miles from the station. The doctor had called for the ambulance through the treble nine system after a male had turned up at the surgery with severe chest pains. On the emergency run north towards Caledonian Road we met with heavy traffic close to Kings Cross station. The congestion made it very difficult to manoeuvre the ambulance around the near stationary vehicles. However, the blue-light run was a lot easier after we got past Kings Cross, and we arrived at the call just nine minutes after receiving the call.

Our patient, a middle-aged male, was sitting upright on a couch in the doctor's consulting room. Standing alongside and holding his hand, his wife was in an obvious state of shock at the events that were quickly unfolding around her.

"Looks like he's had a MI," the doctor said, handing David a letter for the casualty receiving staff. "Would you please run him to the University College. I have rung them, they are expecting you."

Turning to the man he continued, "You'll be alright now Mr Jenkins, you're in good hands and will be in hospital shortly." He placed a hand on the wife's shoulder and finished by saying "He'll be fine, my dear."

In the ambulance, after positioning Mr Jenkins on the trolley bed, David placed the oxygen mask on the patient's face as I sat beside his wife and explained that because of the heavy traffic in the Kings Cross area we would be using the two-tone horns.

"There's no need to be alarmed. It's just that we don't want to be held up in traffic. To be fair to your husband, we want to get him into hospital and made comfortable as soon as possible."

Giving her a reassuring smile as I stood up, walked to the rear of the ambulance, raised the steps, closed the doors, and made my way around to the drivers seat. If anything, the traffic was worse than before as we approached the Kings Cross district, it was at a standstill as far as the eye could see. I slid the connecting door closed to the rear saloon to try and deaden some of the two tone noise that was to drown us over the coming five or so minutes. A path was slowly made for me as I eased *Bloomsbury One* at a little more than walking pace past Kings Cross and St Pancras stations, and along Euston Road to the traffic-lighted junction with Eversholt Street. A further two minutes of noise and I was able to turn the two tones off as I turned our vehicle into Gorden Street that led towards the casualty entrance of the University College Hospital.

We transported a very unwell Mr Jenkins through the casualty area to the resuscitation room where a doctor and nurse helped move him across to the hospital trolley. Within no time at all, Mr Jenkins had been undressed, monitor leads attached and an x-ray machine requested.

"Would you like to book Mr Jenkins into reception for me?" the staff nurse asked David as he handed over the patient's doctor's letter. "Also ask his wife to pop in for a minute, would you?"

"I'll bring her through," I said as we were preparing to leave.

"Thanks," she replied, turning away to continue her duties.

I left Mrs Jenkins in the resuscitation room talking to the staff nurse as I made my back to the ambulance bay to load our trolley bed, and tidy up the rear saloon.

"Cigarette?" I said, offering one to David as he joined me outside the unit.

"No thanks. Don't smoke, don't drink," he replied with a smile.

"God, how boring – no sex either I suppose?" I said with a laugh.

"In moderation – at least twice a year if I'm lucky and if the wife don't know," he said with a hearty laugh.

With a green time from Red Base, I pulled *Bloomsbury One* out of the hospital grounds into Gower Street, and headed back in the direction of our home station.

David seemed to be growing in confidence along with myself, as the late turn week quickly passed by. It had been a busy period, with several overdose calls in the Soho area, a few doctor request removals from home addresses to local casualties or straight to hospital wards, two fire calls, where we removed smoke inhalation victims, several road traffic accident calls with mostly superficial injuries to the casualties.

The last call David and I attended together was quite interesting as it involved going 'inside'. We were called to Pentonville Prison to remove an inmate suffering from appendicitis by doctors request to the Royal Northern Hospital. Security was very tight and the ambulance was searched on our arrival and again on our departure by two warders and one very excited guard dog on a short leash, which sniffed around us as we tried to make the patient comfortable. Eventually, we were allowed to leave the compound through the large pair of wooden security doors that led to the 'outside world'.

I had enjoyed working with David whilst Peter was away. It was strange at first working with a different crewmate, but after the first couple of calls we attended, we soon got into the swing of things working as a crew, and I think it helped me as well, watching somebody else at their approach to the different situations that we faced.

Spring had turned into a nice long summer as Peter and I settled into the routines that surround ambulance work from a busy central station such as Bloomsbury. We were getting used to picking up the 'regulars', getting to know the local police and fire officers, as well as the casualty staff from the nearby hospitals in our catchment area. Most of the calls we received were for sudden illness in the street. Road traffic accidents that we attended were rarely life-threatening situations, most were cuts and grazes from low speed vehicle collisions, but obviously some with multiple fractures, or head or chest injuries occurred from time to time. The few maternity calls we received during this time were straightforward admissions to maternity units of various hospitals in the area. Only once were we nearly caught out by nature by the early arrival of a baby girl to a Indian woman who, when onboard the ambulance, advised me that her labour pains were more frequent than she had let on before we left her house for the admission journey. Her broken English was very limited, but with the help of sign language she informed me it was to be her third child and that she had had a very short labour with her last delivery.

Advising Red Base over the R/T of the situation, we requested they inform the receiving unit of our patients condition and an ETA for *Bloomsbury One*. We later learnt the baby girl was born en-route to the delivery suite from the admission reception. (A bit too close for comfort, I thought to myself at the time). It was to be a couple of months later, when working at New Malden ambulance station, that my first childbirth experience occurred.

The last few weeks I spent working at Bloomsbury training station were very busy, taking in several trips to the mortuaries with beyond-aid patients, including a couple of young overdose casualties, two road traffic victims from a burnt out car that had caught fire after overturning following a collision with a heavy goods vehicle near Euston railway station and four elderly people who had expired during resuscitation attempts following collapse calls.

On the lighter side, during the last week that Peter and I were to work together, we received a call to Grays Inn Road in the Clerkenwell area of Finsbury, where we were informed that a sewer maintenance team worker had slipped off a ledge in a large storm drain, and fractured his leg along with a back injury. On our arrival, we were greeted by a senior fire officer that had just arrived back at street kevel after assessing the situation below ground.

"Hi lads – got a good one for you here," was our greeting as we stepped down from the ambulance.

"Got a workman down below, laying in about a foot of flowing water, complaining of back pains, and he's got a broken leg – Look's like one of your Neil Robertson stretcher jobs to me," he said waving a couple of his crew forward.

"I'll get a couple of my lads to bring the stuff down to you if you can get it out of your motor, then I'll show you where it is," he said pointing to a large open manhole in the middle of the road surrounded by plastic red and white stripped barriers.

After sorting out the equipment we thought we might need below ground, we joined the senior officer on the long descent down a very steep metal ladder to the cold, dark and damp depths below. At the bottom, and after our eyes had become accustomed to the darkness, we moved in line out of a large chamber into a very claustrophobic-looking tunnel just a few feet wide. This led, after twenty yards or so, to a junction where several other openings joined the main sewer. Here we turned right along a larger tunnel about twenty feet tall, with a platform running along one side, which we mounted by means of a small metal ladder. It was while climbing this ladder that Peter slipped and fell headlong into the small stream that was flowing quite fast below us. Turning our torches around towards the splashing noise behind us, the fire officer, one of his colleagues and

I were greeted by the sight of my crewmate standing in the middle of the stream, absolutely soaked from head to foot, minus his hat, and with his hair dripping down both sides of his face.

It couldn't be helped; the three of us stood there in the gloom and just roared our heads off until tears were running down our faces. It's a sight I will never forget, Peter standing there, illuminated by torchlight, his arms outstretched, mouth open and water dripping everywhere. I'm sure I nearly pissed myself with laughter.

With decorum reinstated, Peter was sent back to one of the fire tenders, where the officer said he could change into a pair of slacks and a jumper that were onboard before joining us back underground, this time taking his time in climbing the small ladder. *(Another round of laughter)*.

After a short time Peter made his way back to us at the scene, where we were also joined by a training officer sent out from ambulance headquarters to access the situation below ground, and if need be, call control for further assistance. The casualty, a middle aged sewer worker, was found lying propped up against the wet tunnel wall. He had a compound fracture of his left leg, just above the ankle and was complaining of lower back pain, although he could feel and move his hips and right leg. In all, we were underground for over an hour. It took all of that time to dress and immobilise his fractured leg and position him in the Neil Robertson stretcher, along with a spinal board. We then moved him very slowly along the dank tunnels back to the bottom of the steep metal ladder leading to street level. Two ropes were secured to the stretcher and the ascent back to the daylight was more than a welcome to us all.

In the casualty at University College Hospital, our patient was x-rayed and it was confirmed that the back injury was only bruising to the soft tissue. Apart from the compound fracture to his left leg, he had a fractured patella. He told us before we left, that he had been walking along the raised platform inspecting the brickwork, when he just slipped on the edge, and landed on his back with his leg folded underneath him in the fast-flowing, foul-smelling stream beneath him. It bought a smile to his pain-filled face when we told him of Peter's antics on our way to his rescue. Tears welled up in his big brown eyes as he looked Peter up and down standing there in black slacks and a floppy jumper, both at least two sizes too large. Peter by this time, could see the funny side of things and joined in the laughter at his expense.

A request from red base over the R/T whilst returning to station after another overdose collapse call in the West End asked us to report to the station Training Officer at Waterloo Headquarters as soon as possible. Peter and I wondered what had happened, or what had we done that needed an audience from a headquarters officer.

"Come in gentlemen, take a seat," the officer beckoned to the two chairs placed purposely in front of his large desk.

When we had taken our seats he continued.

"I can't keep you too long – I've told control you're off the road for about twenty minutes, so we'll get on…" Over the following minutes he told Peter and I that our time at Bloomsbury was coming to an end, that the Service was more than pleased with our progress and orders had come through that the pair of us were to be transferred to our respective divisional area stations as from the following Monday morning. I was to report at 0800 hours to the station officer at New Malden ambulance station, and Peter at the same time was to report to his station officer at St Helier main station.

The pair of us were speechless. Although we knew that the day would eventually come when we were moved on, for it to arrive like this, with no warning, came as a bit of a shock.

Looking up at the pair of us, sitting opened mouthed in front of him, he continued.

"I see by looking at your roster, that your last turn of duty at Bloomsbury will be this coming Thursday, so make certain that all your belongings are cleared from the lockers at the station at the end of your shift, so they are completely empty and ready for the new crew that will take over on Friday."

We both nodded our agreement.

"I see you are both off duty on Saturday," he said looking up from the paperwork in front of him.

Again we nodded.

"Well, there's a job for you if you would like to do it – a hospital transfer from the New Charing Cross Hospital to a Private Clinic in Cardiff, using the Lima long distance ambulance. It will give you time when you return to London to pick up anything that you may have left at Bloomsbury –alright?

"Yes sir – we'd love to do it," I answered, after getting an approving look from Peter.

"Good. Report here at six-thirty Saturday morning for the paperwork and the keys to the Lima, and I'll see you both then," he said, standing up.

We made our way through the headquarters building back to *Bloomsbury One* parked in the lower garages, passing several new trainees along with their instructors going through the accident procedures at the makeshift scenes. Only a few months ago we had been doing the same thing, but it seemed a lifetime away now.

Our last turn of duty at the training station turned out to be a very sad day for Peter and I. We had only just taken over *Bloomsbury One* when the bells went for a call, which I took on the red phone just a few minutes after seven o'clock that morning. It took us to a block of council flats in Bingfield street, a mile north of Kings Cross station, where a three month old baby had been found by it's mother in it's cot with no visible life signs. It was sheer pandemonium on our arrival after a very fast run from Bloomsbury. The mother was running up and down the first floor balcony landing' screaming her head off, the father was standing in the hallway of the flat with the infant in his arms rocking the child from side to side. I led the man into the small threadbare lounge, where it took an effort from me to take the baby out of his arms. Placing the infant on the couch, I pulled the white knitted gown away to reveal a very blue, slightly warm infant. Peter and I took it in turns over a period of about ten minutes in resuscitating procedures before deciding to make a run for the ambulance and a dash through the rush hour traffic to the hospital.

The parents joined me in the back of the ambulance, the mother mournfully sobbing to me, "make her breathe – please make her breathe," as I continued to do my best in resuscitating the little girl whilst the vehicle swayed from side to side as Peter manoeuvred *Bloomsbury One* at speed towards the University College Hospital casualty department.

It was the first of several cot-death calls that I was to attend over my service years. Such tragic events never seem to fade from the memory as the years pass on by.

The remainder of the last shift at Bloomsbury was very busy but I found it very difficult to place the early mornings events to the back of my mind as I attended each new casualty that we were called out to.

The last emergency call Peter and I attended together as a crew was to a building site in the City of London, where a labourer had been struck on the head by a falling scaffold pole, causing a fractured skull and leaving him unconscious. After on-site treatment, working amongst piles of rubble, we removed the young man, with help from the site engineer, to the waiting ambulance. A blue call via control was placed for St Bart's Hospital casualty, where after a short journey, the waiting crash team were ready for our arrival in the prepared resuscitation room.

It was quite sad walking away from Bloomsbury ambulance station after that eventful last day. So much had happened in the couple of months I had been there. I had learnt an awful lot about human nature, seen a lot of hardships, witnessed pain and pleasure, seen men cry, and how brave little children can be when faced with serious domestic violence. I had also made some very good friends amongst the other two emergency services, the local casualty department staff and the other crews that were manning the Bloomsbury ambulances whilst I was there.

Peter and I met at Headquarters early on Saturday morning ready for the trip to Wales in the Austin Princess Lima ambulance, a journey we were both looking forward to.

I won the toss to drive down to Cardiff, leaving Peter to take the wheel for the empty return trip, After picking up the paperwork and keys for the Lima we made our way to the basement garage to collect the vehicle.

"Very smooth," was my comment as I eased the high-powered, three-litre automatic through the early morning traffic towards Charing Cross Hospital at Hammersmith in North West London.

"Grab a breakfast in the canteen while you're waiting," the ward sister said after telling us that our patient wouldn't be ready for another half an hour. We didn't need telling twice and made our way to the top floor restaurant to tuck into a full English breakfast.

Our patient, a forty-four-year-old female, had suffered a fractured pelvis in a road traffic accident four weeks earlier at a Chiswick roundabout, whilst on her way from South Wales to visit friends in London. We loaded the lady aboard the Lima and slowly pulled away from the hospital, joined the westbound traffic leading to the M4 motorway and South Wales.

The journey west was very smooth, and the vehicle was a pleasure to drive as the miles rolled by with no effort. We made one stop at a motorway services centre for a break, where I returned to the ambulance with three plastic cups of tea to enjoy in the rear of the Lima. Our patient was very outgoing and a real pleasure to talk to. We learnt that she had been a dancer on the London stages, then on the cruise ships before finally starting her own school in Cardiff from which at least two well-known actors had graduated.

With good written instructions, I had no trouble finding the clinic a few miles North of Cardiff City Centre, where we were met by the patient's husband and a couple of her students from the school who made a real theatrical show of the arrival, causing embarrassment to the waiting medical staff and ourselves. After making the lady comfortable in a private room, Peter and I were offered tea, coffee and a pile of sandwiches, which we enjoyed in the plush surroundings of the clinic before setting off for our return journey to the Capital.

The trip back East along the M4 corridor into Greater London was again a very nice smooth run and I felt quite at ease relaxing in the passenger seat as Peter drove the Lima at a steady, controlled speed, matching the flow of traffic which grew ever heavier as we neared 'the Smoke'.

"Lima One – Red Base – Over." I spoke into the microphone as we passed London airport.

"Lima One – Go Ahead."

"Lima One – Back in the Area, Passing London Airport Eastbound – Over."

"Thank you Lima One – Continue to HQ – Over."

"Roger – Over"

I replaced the microphone to it's position at the side of the radio set. An hour later we had refuelled, cleaned and garaged the Lima, completed the paperwork, changed into civilian clothing and were ready to enjoy a drink or two in the local public houses in the Waterloo area.

"You picking your cars up tomorrow?" the station officer said entering the changing room.

"Yes Gov!" I said looking around at him.

"Good. Anyway, I've been told to thank you both for what you have achieved here, and at the training station, also I would like to wish you both the very best at your new postings."

"Thank you sir," we both answered with slight embarrassment.

"Have a nice drink the pair of you, enjoy yourselves and thanks again."

The officer turned and left the room.

We did have a good night as we toured the local pubs, ending at the New Crown and Cushion public house, where a couple of months earlier, we had celebrated passing the headquarters examinations along with our class of students. I said my goodbyes to Peter whilst standing on the pavement outside the pub after closing time on that Saturday night, knowing we would never work again as a crew, but no doubt we would see each other in passing, at various hospitals in South London in the years to come.

Peter was to leave the London Ambulance Service sixteen months later, after losing his wife in childbirth with their second child. He later emigrated to Canada, where he remarried and became a teacher at a village junior school.

The author, along with John and Martin, the other leading ambulancemen at the Oval main station.

Richmond Ambulance Station - 1970s. The author between the two Brians, shortly before his move to Streatham ambulance station.

PART IV

New Malden, Tolworth and Richmond

Monday morning started as wet and windy, but with the promise of warm sunshine later in the day to greet the arrival of early August 1975. After parking up behind the ambulance station at New Malden, I allowed myself plenty of time to make my way across to the office block to meet Mr Whiteside the station officer for the second time that year.

"Come in Mr Kinsley, take a seat," the officer said, pointing with his pen to the chair placed in front of his desk. I sat and glanced around the room at the photographs of bygone days in the service of the officer sitting in front of me whilst he leafed through the documents in a folder bearing my name on the front cover. Several times he turned back a few sheets to read again the previous pages. I was just thinking to myself 'there seems to be a lot of paperwork just for five months in the service' when my thoughts were interrupted by the clearing of his throat and replacing the folder on the desktop.

"A good report from headquarters," he said, nodding towards the closed folder in front of him.

"Enjoy Bloomsbury?" he asked, adding before I could reply, "I used to work out of there years ago when we first took the station over from the fire brigade. A busy place at the best of times."

"Yes sir," I said, crossing my arms.

"It'll be a bit different here John – not quite so mad as Bloomsbury. I'll be placing you on the relief roster, which means you will be doing three weeks of white work on one of the day coaches, followed by three weeks of relief duties for sickness or leave at the accident stations, that's here at New Malden and also at Tolworth and Richmond, they are the satellite stations – alright?"

"Yes sir," I replied.

"As for today, I want you to spend it with John Davis, the early-turn leading ambulanceman, who will give you all the details of your roster and will probable take you out to Tolworth and Richmond during the day to have a look around."

He stood up, obviously to end our meeting.

"Thank you sir," I said as I stood up, turned and made my exit.

I had an uneasy feeling as I crossed the yard in the drizzle and approached the old-fashioned buildings housing the mess and watch rooms for the New Malden crews. I had that same gut feeling as I did on my first morning all those months ago when I first walked into Bloomsbury station with Peter for the very first time. Just for a brief moment, the dozen or so personnel in the room stopped talking as I entered their domain and closed the door behind me. My apprehension diminished slowly over the following hour as John Davis the

L.A.M. (Leading Ambulanceman) made himself known to me and briefly introduced me to the various individuals, some of whom were already leaving the room to start their day turns on the non-emergency vehicles.

As that first hour slowly passed, only seven of us were left in the room, apart from me, two emergency crews, that were manning *Malden One and Two* frontline ambulances, a relief crewmember, and John the L.A.M.

After the third mug of tea during the morning, following a tour of the station I was informed that the crews would shortly be moved from the old buildings with their cramped conditions, to a new Portacabin block that was being erected on the other side of the complex.

John asked me to join him on a trip around to the other two stations that were under the control of New Malden Main Station. After loading the staff car with a pile of clean blankets for the two stations, John pulled the white Morris Marina service car out into Kingston Road and headed for the Kingston by–pass and the Surbiton area. Tucked neatly beneath an office block behind the Broadway at Tolworth is the small sixteen-hour ambulance station. *(The night cover for this area is covered from New Malden).* Two fully equipped vehicles work from the small station, one on standby for accidents and emergencies whilst the other works the catchment area on 'white' (non-urgent) clinic appointments for those that are unable to use a sitting-type day ambulance. Being fully equipped, this ambulance can be called into service as an accident vehicle by Red Base at any time when the area is busy or uncovered. Both the vehicles were away from station when we dropped off the supplies and fresh blankets, so I didn't see any new faces that I might be working with over the coming weeks. With the Marina's boot filled with the soiled blankets from the station, John was ready to head for Richmond. The drizzle had at last ceased and the warmth returned as the sun blazed down through the now breaking cloud cover, giving that nice to be alive feeling as people returned to the sidewalks in summer garb and sunglasses.

John drove the staff car away from the Surbiton district and on through the back streets of Kingston upon Thames towards Richmond Park. The journey through the park was beautiful, with visitors and locals alike making the most of the promised sunshine, also very different for me. Only days ago, I had been dashing around Central London in a highly polluted environment – this was heaven.

Leaving the park at Richmond Gate, John moved the Marina down the Star and Garter Hill towards Richmond town centre, where he turned right into Kings Road and along to the very modern looking ambulance station down on the left hand side. Pulling into the large frontage, John parked the staff car in front of the six bay garage area.

The single-storey station, built only a couple of years previously, was indeed very different to anything I had seen before. An open-plan mess room with a large picture window led through to a Swedish style kitchen area, fitted out with all mod-cons. A corridor ran from the kitchen along the back of the station, with doors leading off to toilets, shower room and the stores finally ending with a door leading back into the garages. Although six vehicle bays had been built, only three ambulances were stationed there. *Richmond One*, the twenty four hour emergency vehicle, *Richmond Three*, another emergency ambulance, but only manned for sixteen hours a day, and *Richmond Five*, used for non-emergency white work in the surrounding area over an eight hour day, but again fully equipped for emergency work if the need arose. Back in the mess-room after the grand tour, John and I settled down to enjoy a mug of coffee with the number three crew, the other two crews being out on the road. Looking around the room, a large, well-stocked tropical fish tank graced one wall, opposite was the large map of Richmond's area alongside the desk with the mandatory telephones and message pads, a well-positioned television set competed the furnishings. It was then that I thought to myself that this was the station I would like to work from and decided immediately that I would apply to be put on the waiting list as soon as possible, knowing that in all probability it would be a long wait.

The following morning saw the start of my three weeks of white non-emergency work. I was crewed with Peter Christie, a middle-aged, experienced ambulanceman who had been with the service for many years. Our work over these weeks consisted of collecting and returning patients either from their home address or from nursing homes in the area, transporting them in good time to meet clinic appointments at a mixture of hospitals in London. Some of the trips, took me back into the fume-filled area that I had worked from Bloomsbury and it was no surprise when we had to pull over to allow passage for one of the accident vehicles weaving its way through the heavy traffic, no doubt on another overdose call to the West End.

I enjoyed the white work, it made a nice change not having the pressure of not knowing what you would be faced with when turning out to a treble nine call. Peter and I took it in turns, day and day about to do the driving, either a twelve-seater coach with a tail lift or a standard ambulance for stretcher cases. Our patients were a mixture from all backgrounds, most of them elderly and cheerful, despite their medical conditions, all of whom looked forward to the outings arranged for them aboard the service vehicles. I would get to know many of them quite well in times to come, amongst them some amputee's who we transported back and forth to the limb fitting centre at Queen Mary's Hospital, Roehampton. These individuals to me are a credit to the human race and they always had a smile and good word to greet us, despite the pain and physical incapacity they faced daily.

The first three weeks of white work came to a close too quickly and from the following Monday I was to report at 1500 hours to New Malden, to start a week of late-turn relief duties. Provided all the late turn crews had reported for duty, relief duties consisted of nothing more than cleaning, sorting stores, collecting and delivering blankets to the two outlying stations, and any other work that the L.A.M. felt needed doing. These duties continued throughout the week until the Saturday, when I was advised as I arrived on station that I was to be crewed up with Clive Morris on *Malden One*, due to his colleague reporting in sick.

That gut feeling had returned. I was to work with a complete stranger who, like Peter, had many years of experience behind him. I was certain I was going to make a hash of things. Whilst doing the vehicle check, I noticed Clive was placing extra equipment in the ambulance, a black hand-held type case that held intubation and resuscitation gear, also a metal-type box which was loaded with infusion packs. Clive was a paramedic, one of the first to be trained in the London Ambulance Service.

"You alright John?" he asked as we neared the end of the check.

"Yeah fine," I replied without looking up from the checklist in front of me.

"Good, I'll go and make a pot of tea while you refuel. See you back in the mess-room in a minute."

He jumped down from the rear doors, turned and made his way towards the station's old building.

After refuelling *Malden One* I re-parked the vehicle in the marked bay and opened the back doors to help ventilate the rear saloon on what was now turning out to be a very hot and sultry afternoon. The first call of the shift came in at a quarter to four, the alarm bells springing into life breaking the smalltalk between the crews and the duty L.A.M. who had joined us in the mess-room. The call was to Kingston Market Place, where an elderly female had collapsed and had been removed to the shade of a nearby butchers shop behind a row of stalls. After Clive had examined the old lady, we conveyed her along with her friend to Kingston Hospital, where we placed her in the care of the casualty staff.

A very brief thunderstorm had occurred whilst we were in the casualty department, and it felt nice for a short time at least to feel the dampness in the air as we returned outside to our waiting ambulance. Returning to station along the quickly drying roads Red Base called us over the R/T.

"Malden One Report – Over."

"Kingston Road – Approaching Station," Clive said in reply.

"Call Red accident for you if your ready Malden One – Over."

"Go Ahead."

"Thank You Malden One – it's a Call Red RTA – you're the second ambulance to the Kingston by-pass, south-bound, close to the Hook underpass – Tolworth One is on scene – my initials Delta Foxtrot – timed to you at 1637 hours Malden One – Over.

Clive read back the call back to the controller as I switched on the warning devices and headed the ambulance in the direction of the by-pass. Our fast run south bound came almost to a standstill as we met the traffic build up from the accident ahead. A traffic police car directed us to follow him across to the northbound lanes, and with a lot of caution we travelled against the flow of oncoming vehicles heading for Central London. I followed the police car as far as the Hook roundabout, then backtracked along the now empty southbound lanes to the accident site.

Tolworth One was pulling away as we neared a scene of absolute carnage. Wreckage was spread across all three lanes of the by-pass. What remained of a car was rammed underneath the rear of a heavy goods lorry, with only the car boot showing undamaged. Fire service crews had secured the rear of the car with ropes to the front of one of their engines, and a police officer was in the process of attempting to move the lorry under power forward so the rescue of the occupants of the crushed car could go ahead. It was the lorry driver and a passing female motorist that the *Tolworth One* crew had removed from the scene, both suffering from severe shock.

Slowly the lorry edged forward, inches at a time, until the fire officer in charge held up his arms, and shouting at the same time to the police driver to stop and secure the brakes. Enough room had been obtained for the rescue to commence. Clive and the senior fireman were the first to approach the wreckage, leaving the remaining firemen, some policeman, and myself standing there in silence waiting for the forthcoming instructions.

"John, get my boxes from the ambulance!" Clive shouted to me without turning his head away from his captured vision. Within moments I was at his side with the two boxes he had requested. 'What a mess,' I thought, as I surveyed the scene before me.

"This one's still alive," he said, as he ripped the shirt sleeve from a young male who was pinned behind the buckled steering wheel. The female beside him was obviously dead; she had been decapitated and her lower limbs had been pushed upwards across her light blue summer costume, now blood-soaked, both limbs having come to rest in a position close to her rounded chest.

Clive worked at a steady methodical pace and in no time at all the young male had been intubated, infused, and a large head and chest wound dressed.

"I'll leave you in charge of the re-sus bag John, keep it going at about seventeen a minute," Clive said to me, moving out from behind the casualty and allowing me enough room to take his place.

I squatted in the cramped conditions, bagging the patient as instructed whilst Clive helped the fire officers cut away the metalwork from around us to make the extraction as easy as possible.

More senior officers from the fire service and the police turned up at the site along with our own leading ambulanceman from New Malden as the rescue was reaching it's climax.

"Doing alright John?" the L.A.M. asked, making his attendance known to me.

"Yes gov," I replied, trying to alter my position as my legs were cramping.

"Good, won't be long now, nearly done," he said moving away to join Clive.

Very slowly the young man was lifted by the rescuers up and over the twisted metalwork and onto a waiting trolley bed that had been prepared by the *Malden Three* crew who had arrived a few minutes after the L.A.M.

With the patient loaded, and the leading ambulanceman aboard to assist Clive, I pulled away from the scene and headed for Kingston Hospital casualty.

"Blue call to Kingston," Clive shouted through from the back.

"Right," I called back as I lifted the microphone.

"Priority."

"Go Ahead Priority."

"Malden One – Blue Kingston Hospital – young male unconscious with multiple injuries, ETA of eight minutes – Over.

The controller read the request back as I replaced the microphone and concentrated on the task in hand. The heavens opened up with another cloudburst as a thunderstorm moved in above us. I left the by-pass at the Hook roundabout, joining the heavy traffic on the Hook Road and with the two tones and blue lights running I moved the ambulance at a speed fast enough in the conditions to reach the designated hospital as soon as possible.

With the casualty unloaded and transported to the resuscitation room at the Kingston casualty, I left Clive and the L.A.M. working with the crash room staff as I removed the trolley bed and soiled equipment back to our ambulance and started cleaning up. Twenty minutes later with the vehicle back in it's ready state, I walked back down the corridor and slowly opened the crash room doors and entered to join my colleagues who were now standing back to watch the medical team going about their business. The male was lying naked on the hospital trolley with leads and tubes attached – his injuries now more obvious. Clive walked over to join me as I stood there taking in the scene before me.

"Alright John?" he asked.

"Fine," I said, adding, "the ambulance is back to square one."

"Right. This chap's lucky to be alive," he said nodding towards our patient.

"Look's like a fractured skull, both legs broken, and internal chest injuries where he was pinned behind the steering wheel. I didn't think we would get him here in time. A lucky, lucky lad."

Clive turned for the exit with the L.A.M. and me behind him and we made our way back through the busy corridor to *Malden One* now waiting in the ambulance bay bathed in brilliant warm sunshine, not a cloud in the sky.

We learnt later that evening on a return trip to the casualty with an abdo-pains patient, that our road accident victim from the by-pass had responded well to the crash room treatment and was still in theatre on the top floor. We were told that the couple in the car were on the way to the south coast for their honeymoon following their marriage earlier that morning somewhere in north London. The young bride was removed to the Kingston Hospital Purple

Annex by the *Malden Three* crew after a difficult extraction
by the rescue teams. Her horrific injuries and the time taken
to remove the life extinct body left all the crews in a state
of understandable shock. It was believed the new husband
lost control of the high powered hire car during a heavy
downpour in one of the storms that were passing through
Southern England on that hot sultry afternoon. Witnesses
stated that the car had skidded, aquaplaned and slid under
the rear of the near stationary heavy goods vehicle which
had slowed down because of limited visibility caused by the
torrential downpour.

So very sad – they were just a few hours into a new life
together. So young. Such a waste.

My first accident shift at New Malden had certainly
been eventful and witnessing a paramedic going about
his work in such an unflappable manner had left me with
nothing but admiration, hoping that one day in the future
I could achieve that same level of care, consideration and
concentration that was shown on that hot summer Saturday
afternoon.

The months were flying by, and the gorgeous summer
and autumn had given away to early frosts morning and
evening as the winter moved in to take its grip on the capital.
My home life was also in the process of change. I had moved
out of my home in Mitcham and moved in with Jacqueline
(later to be my second wife), where we shared a flat on the
large estate at New Addington on the outskirts of Croydon
in south London.

My duty roster over these months saw me covering accident and emergency shifts at Richmond, Tolworth and New Malden. It was good to be working with a mixture of personnel at these stations, and I learnt a great deal by observing my experienced crewmates. Each went about the business of call-outs and the treatment of patients in his own particular way, giving me the benefit of choosing for myself what I perceived as the best approach and treatment to apply to my own patients. It was during this period of time that I was informed by the station officer, Mr Whiteside, that my posting to Richmond station had come through and that I would be joining the station crews within the next few weeks. I was elated.

One of my last night shifts out of New Malden before my transfer to Richmond came through, was a shift I worked with a newcomer down from headquarters, who had only been based on station for just over a week. It was a night shift I will never forget...

My new crewmate for the night was John Little, a dark-haired 22-year-old who had been on the service for four months and, like myself, had worked out of Bloomsbury station before his transfer to New Malden. After carrying out the mandatory vehicle check, recharging the hot water bottles and placing them between the red trolley blankets, leaving the in-built paraffin heater running at low speed to keep the ambulance warm, we returned to the welcome heat of the mess-room and a mug of soup.

The first two calls of the night followed in quick succession, the first, a slight head injury to an elderly female who had tripped over the pavement whilst making her exit from a local public house in Kingston Town centre. The second, was a call to a fourth floor flat, again in the Kingston area, where a 40-year-old male had collapsed with chest pains. After a difficult removal, we transported him to the local casualty department.

The third call of the night came through on the red phone as we were relaxing in the very warm mess room of the new Portacabin building.

"Call For You Malden."

"Go Ahead," I said, at the same time picking up the ever-ready biro.

"Had a bloke on the phone this end, saying his girlfriend's having a baby, the address given as Sanger Avenue, Chessington North – He said it's the squatters house – that's all we've got – so if you can give us a shout when you've found it – OK – Timed to you 0235 hours – Mike Bravo.

After reading the call back to Mike Bravo, John and I left the warmth of the station to be faced by a bone-chilling wind with sleet falling illuminated by the yard floodlights. Quickly climbing aboard the waiting warm ambulance, John fired the engine, and in no time at all we were heading through the deserted sleet covered streets towards the Chessington area.

We entered Sanger Avenue and slowly drove down the road looking out for the mentioned Squatters house. From beneath a broken street lamp, a young man dressed only in jeans and a thin cotton shirt came running up to us shouting that his girlfriend was having a baby. He grabbed my arm as I opened the sliding door.

"Hurry up! – Quick!" he urged. With torch in hand and first aid satchel slung across my shoulder, I followed him through a broken down front door, up two flights of unlit stairs, through to a stench-filled back room where half a dozen candles placed on the Victorian mantelpiece illuminated the scene before me.

A young girl (just seventeen, I later learned) was lying in the recumbent position on a dirty four foot mattress placed in the middle of the floor. The room was freezing and I was physically shaking as I looked quickly around to take stock of the situation. The girl was on her back, uncovered, crying, along with short sharp screams that echoed in the near darkness. Her knees were bent, and she was in the process of defecation, I shared her immediate embarrassment.

Kneeling down beside her and with her nodding approval, I made a quick examination of her lower half, finding that indeed she was in the second stage of labour.

I asked John to get on to Red Base on the R/T, and get an Obstetrics Team here as soon as possible, and tell them that the birth is imminent, also to knock the people up next door, we want some clean towels, and hot water. Bring up from the ambulance, the maternity pack, some warm blankets, hot water bottles, and the Enternox gas.

"What's your name?" I asked the frightened tearful girl.

"Jane," she answered following another painful contraction.

I explained to her as briefly as I could, what we would be doing, also that help was on the way, and will be with us shortly.

The neighbour, a middle aged woman with only a dressing gown on over her nightdress followed John into the room carrying between them the requested items from the ambulance.

Within minutes, and with the help of the woman, I had cleaned the excrement away from the lower half of the embarrassed sobbing girl, all the time doing my best to reassure her, adding that the midwife and doctor would be with us very shortly.

Mother nature herself had different ideas, however, and amongst the short sharp screams and the straining of pushing down from the mother-to-be, a baby's head appeared from the birth channel. With help from the pain relief gas administered by my colleague, Jane gave a final downward thrust as I eased the infant's shoulders through the now torn vaginal area. Easing the umbilical cord from around the baby's neck, I quickly cleared the mucus from the airway just as the newborn let out a welcome shrill to it's new cold surroundings.

"What is it?" Jane asked attempting to sit up.

"It's a boy," I replied as the neighbour helped me wrap a warm towel around the infant, then placing it on the new mothers tummy for her to hold.

"Jane… the cord is still attached, so try very hard to lie still for me will you?" I said to the crying mother as I stood up to stretch my cramped legs and wipe away the sweat from my forehead that had appeared despite it being a very cold night.

The Obstetrics team, a midwife, a doctor, and a nurse arrived at the scene a few minutes later luck had been on our side in as much the team had been fortunate that a Surrey ambulance was ready to leave Kingston Hospital when they were instructed to convey the team to the address at Chessington before returning to their own station at Epsom.

With more illumination in the room from the extra hand-lamps, the team set about completing the task of cutting the cord, removing the afterbirth, inserting a couple of stitches and setting up an intravenous drip. When they had finished, John and I had the task of conveying the patient on a carrying chair down the dark staircase, through the broken door and out into the welcome warmth of *Malden One*.

At Kingston Hospital's maternity unit, Jane and her new son were settled into a side room as nurses and a doctor went about their post-natal duties.

"What's your name," Jane asked me as we were preparing to make our exit from the room.

"John, John Kinsley – why?" I inquired, turning back to face her in the white-sheeted bed.

"I would like to name the baby after you, if you don't mind," she said, a little embarrassed.

A lump came to my throat as I walked back towards her bedside.

"That's nice, I would be honoured," I said as I lifted her hand to shake. "I must go now, the nurses have a lot to do, so take care of yourself and little Johnny."

I smiled as I replaced her hand on the bedcovers, turned away, and left the room. I really felt choked as I walked back along the corridor, down the staircase, through the heavy plastic swing doors and out into the cold night air to join John who was putting the finishing touches to cleaning up the business-end of the ambulance.

One more call that night took us to an address in New Malden – to put back to bed an elderly lady who had slipped whilst going to the toilet and was unable to get up from the floor. After assuring us she was uninjured, we replaced her in bed, made her a cup of tea and left her quite content, sitting upright propped against half a dozen pillows sipping her beverage.

Trying to sleep after a quick shower and a light breakfast was next to impossible after such a night. My mind kept replaying the events that had unfolded in those cold, dark hours that had given me such a rewarding and unforgettable experience of a lifetime. At long last sleep took its hold and I slid into a happy oblivion.

My home life with new partner Jacqueline had settled into a happy domestic routine. Jackie had applied and been accepted for a nursing post at Caine Hill mental hospital close to Coulsdon on the southern outskirts of Greater

London. We had some wonderful evenings together as we ploughed through the medical books and journals, asking each other questions, all the time gaining much-needed knowledge to assist us in our individual professions.

I had, by this time, settled into my new station at Richmond, the only drawback being the fifty mile round trip to each turn of duty, most of the time in heavy traffic conditions. The shifts at Richmond rotated around accident and emergency turns, with every fifth week working *Richmond Five* on white non-emergency patient journeys. I worked with various crew members during these shifts, until one beautiful spring morning, one chap asked me if I would like to crew up with him on a permanent basis. From that morning until two and a half years later when I moved from Richmond, I worked with Johnny Marsh, a five-foot-two, blond-haired, goatee-bearded individual, who was, despite his height and build, very strong and a real pleasure to work with.

Richmond was a very busy station compared to New Malden and Tolworth, and John and I had our fair share of the run-of-the-mill calls in the large catchment area. Stabbings were now becoming nightly events, as was serious domestic violence within the large gay community that existed on our patch. Road traffic accidents were, in most cases, high-speed collisions that occurred from time to time on the dual-carriageway sections of the Chertsey and Twickenham roads, often resulting in life-threatening injuries and in some cases, fatalities.

One Saturday night, John and I had only just booked on duty when we were called out to an RTA that had occurred on the south side of Hammersmith Bridge. A father and son had lost their lives, when their Ford Escort van had run into the back of a bus at speed. Both were beyond medical aid when we reached them, after fire service personnel had cut away the roof of the van so we could gain access. Following this tragic accident, whilst on the way back to Richmond from the mortuary at New Charing Cross Hospital, we were called over the R/T to attend another RTA that had taken place in Roehampton Lane, close to Queen Mary's Hospital. The scene that greeted us on our arrival was absolute chaos – a mass of blue lights from police and fire tenders lit up the night sky. Two badly damaged motorcycles, twenty yards apart, graced the damp road surface. Both had collided with a traffic island whilst racing each other from Barnes Common up to the Kingston Road. The young male rider of one of the machines, along with his female pillion passenger, had received fatal injuries. Both were covered in blankets bought to the scene by staff of the nearby casualty department. The second rider, another male, was being treated by a doctor and nurse as we approached.

"Hello doc," I said kneeling down beside him.

"I think he's broken his back, I'm not taking his helmet off yet, but I don't like the look of this," the doctor said, pointing to a mixture of blood and cerebrospinal fluid flowing from beneath the badly scared helmet.

"Have you got one of your split stretchers onboard?" he asked looking around at me.

"A scoop stretcher, yes, we'll get it," I said, standing up.

John and I positioned the scoop under the victim, and with help from the surrounding firemen lifted him onto a hospital trolley that had been wheeled out ready by the medical staff from the casualty department. When he was examined in the casualty unit, his injuries were indeed as the doctor had feared at the scene: an obvious fractured skull with seepage still evident and the spinal column well out of alignment from mid chest to pelvis.

Outside the hospital, a Putney crew were in the process of removing the male fatality, leaving John and I the job of shifting the black-haired female onto our trolley bed.

It was a sorry sight in the mortuary as we slid our young female victim across from our trolley bed to a metal-topped hospital trolley. Her long black hair was matted with drying blood and her once beautiful face was a mess. The police officer who accompanied us to the Purple Annex told us that the two young fatalities had been riding with no crash helmets. It was now understandable how both had received such horrific injuries.

The other rider, we later learnt, ended up as a paraplegic and was later transferred to a mental institution due to irreversible brain damage.

The night still had one surprise in store for us as we were returning to station after a maternity admission to Queen

Mary's Hospital at just a few minutes after six fifteen, when the R/T burst into life requesting our position.

"Upper Richmond Road, approaching Clifford Avenue," I replied.

"Call Red RTA if you're ready Richmond One."

"Go Ahead – Over."

"It's a Call Red RTA outside the Watneys Brewery, Mortlake High Street – female knocked down – police on scene – timed to you at 0618 hours – Alpha Delta – Richmond One – Over."

As I read the call back, John was already turning our vehicle into Clifford Avenue and pointing the ambulance in the Mortlake direction.

A policeman walked up to us as we pulled up outside the brewery.

"It looks like a fatal mate," he said, as we stepped down from the vehicle.

"I don't believe this," John said to me as we fell into line behind the police officer as he led us towards a stationary continental heavy goods lorry.

"Me too – it's unbelievable," I replied.

"Under there," the policeman said, bending down and pointing under the lorry.

I crawled the few feet under the lorry to make what assessment I could. It was more than obvious that an elderly female had received fatal injuries and was well beyond medical aid.

The fire brigade personnel raised the front of the heavy lorry and assisted us in a messy removal of the casualty to our ambulance. After a short run we were once again at Queen Mary's Hospital in Roehampton.

"One good thing, she didn't know much about it," the doctor said, pulling the red blanket back over the woman after making his examination in the back of the ambulance. Signing the LA-4 form he bid us good-by and stepped down from the vehicle to return to his domain behind the swing doors leading to the casualty, leaving us, once again, with a trip to the Purple Annex.

What a night! It was a relief to get home, laze in a warm bath before breakfast and hopefully get some restful sleep. Five fatal road accident victims in one night for one crew was, to say the least, unusual. Fingers crossed, it was something that would never be repeated.

Winter had once again turned into spring and it was nice to be back in shirtsleeve order as the hot days of summer arrived at long last. It was a real pleasure working with Johnny Marsh – we almost seemed to have an understanding of each other's thoughts as we went about our daily tasks. There was no need to ask for certain equipment, it was already at hand when needed, or to worry where the other was when we had to split up at incidents where multiple casualties were involved. It was a great working relationship, one we carried through to our off-duty hours when John and his wife Gretal along with Jackie and I, enjoyed many happy social outings.

With the arrival of summer came daily reports in the newspapers and on the radio and television news bulletins that IRA bombing activities were increasing in mainland Britain. Reports showed casualties being led away to waiting ambulances by emergency crews or unfortunate victims covered from head to toe in blankets, never to see another sunrise.

Our turn to attend a bombing incident came one sunny afternoon when we were called from station to back up the ambulances already on scene at the Olympia exhibition hall in Kensington West London. We joined a line of ambulances waiting to be called forward to attend the injured, and transport the casualties to the designated hospitals in the area.

We treated three casualties removed from the smoking building that afternoon: a police officer who we had to restrain because he was trying to claw his face with his hands to remove numerous glass splinters that had been embedded in the soft facial tissue; a woman with severe leg injuries, and lastly, a ten-year-old American girl on holiday in England with her parents, both of whom were still reported missing in the exhibition hall. Her injuries consisted of lacerations to her legs and neck, with a slither of glass embedded in her cheek.

It was a busy afternoon for the emergency services, the constant howl of two tones as vehicles left and arrived at the scene, along with Scotland Yard's bomb squad cars and vans, full of personnel dressed in overalls, ready to go about their set routines, which were now becoming much to regular.

Despite the bombings that were going on in London, around this time an amusing incident occurred one morning... Following a Bank holiday weekend, we received a call on station to attend an explosion that had taken place in Brentford High Street, with reports coming in of multiple casualties.

Heavy rain started to fall as we took off at speed towards the call area, joining up with a convoy of emergency vehicles rushing to the scene as we crossed Kew Bridge from the south side. We stared in amazement as we came to a stand in the High Street where a cloud of smoke hung over the area. A dozen bodies were scattered across the roadway in front of us, and in a deathly silence we slowly approached the casualties. The 'casualties' turned out to be shop window dummies, blown out into the street from Burtons the tailors, following an explosion in a nearby baker's shop.

The blast was not an IRA act of aggression as first thought – a build-up of gas that had accumulated over the Bank holiday weekend had ignited when the bakery was re-opened.

Three casualties required treatment following the blast – none serious, only cuts and bruises and a little hurt pride at having caused so much chaos.

John was on leave when a similar event took place, I had been crewed for the day with a relief man from New Malden, Howard Fletcher, a tall, likable young man who I was told used to be an actor in the television series *Please Sir*. After booking on at Richmond we were taken out by staff car to West Hill near Putney to relieve the night crew on *Richmond One*, that had been placed in a holding position due to a hostage situation that was taking place in a ground floor flat a few hundred yards away. Before the night crew left in the staff car, they told us that refreshments were available from a mobile police canteen nearby. As Howard was going to do the vehicle check, I said I would find the canteen and grab us something to eat and drink.

I jumped down from the ambulance, and started to make my way along the deserted sealed off street, when suddenly I was grabbed and pulled headlong into some thick bushes on my left hand side.

"Where the fuck are you going?" a growling six-foot uniformed policeman shouted at me, hanging onto my jacket sleeve with one hand and a telescopic-sighted rifle in the other.

"Getting some grub…" I answered, nervously, trying too pull away.

"Not this way, you prick! You're in the line of fire! Over there…" he said, pointing to the clearing behind him after he had let go of my jacket. With my tail between my legs, I moved off, feeling highly embarrassed, to find the so-called well-stocked canteen, making sure that on my return I gave the hidden marksman a wide detour. Howard was in stitches when I explained what had happened, and no doubt the story found its way to many ambulance service mess-rooms over the coming months.

All hell broke loose a couple of hours later when police officers stormed the ground floor flat, calling for us by hand signals to pull the ambulance down to a grass verge in front of the hostage building. Following two plainclothes officers into the flat, we found a balding man with a head injury lying in the middle of the floor. Sitting astride him was a heavily-built plainclothes officer, preventing the offender from moving. A young woman with two children was being escorted out of the room by two uniformed WPCs – they had been the hostages, held by the gunman for the last twelve hours.

"You going to behave yourself Richard?" the burly police-man said to the man underneath him.

"Yeah."

"Good. These two ambulancemen are going to have a look at you, so behave yourself alright?"

"Yeah – yeah, I'll be alright, I'll behave myself," the captive said aloud."

"It'll need a few stitches," I said after we had examined him and applied a pressure pad dressing.

"He will only leave here on one condition – that he is carried out secured to a stretcher," the officer in charge stated.

"That's a bit dramatic for this type of injury," I said.

"That's what the gov' wants."

With Richard secured to the stretcher, we started to make our exit from the ground floor flat, and went straight into view of the waiting media. The area was surrounded by a battery of cameras of all shapes and sizes, waiting their chance to catch a glimpse of the hostage-taker.

With shutters clicking away, and film cameras recording the event, we loaded Richard aboard *Richmond One*, closed the rear doors, and with a strong police escort plus two outriders, we pulled away heading for Queen Mary's Hospital. (Footage taken during this removal was used later in the opening credits of the television series *The Gentle Touch*.)

My divorce had been settled, so Jackie and myself planned for a December wedding knowing that we would spend the rest of our lives together, come what may. It was on December 21st 1977, a wet and windy day, that Jacqueline and I tied the knot at Croydon Registry Office, in front of some close and dear friends. My new wife and I spent the evening at the King's Arms in Richmond, amongst some ambulance colleagues, and although money was tight, we all had a wonderful evening.

One evening in the mess-room at Richmond when John and I were alone on the station I told him that I was thinking of moving to a station nearer home. I was fed up with the large amount of travelling to and from work and, although I had used my divorce settlement as a deposit on a terraced three-bedroomed house near Thorton Heath, on the outskirts of Croydon, it was still a time-consuming journey each working day. John responded by saying that he had been waiting for the right time to tell me that he and Gretal had decided to move away from London and that he had received a favourable reply from Wiltshire Ambulance Service regarding a transfer. After working together for what seemed forever, we realised our partnership was to end – but not before some more memorable events had taken place…

Richmond Three normally stood down from duty at 2300 hours, but if the off-going crew were willing, Red Base would keep them on duty for a few more hours and utilize them to attend incidents in any area that is temporarily without cover or has all its crews occupied. On one such night we were instructed to make our way to Hammersmith Broadway and stand by to await further orders on the R/T. We hadn't been in position long when we were called to a stabbing incident at a small hotel in Trebovir Road, behind Earls Court Underground station. On our arrival, John and I were led down a dark staircase by a long-legged blonde-haired beauty. We entered a room where music was blaring at loud volume and it took several attempts, by shouting, to get it turned off. I looked around the room, which was in almost total darkness; it was full of girls.

I asked the nearest girl to turn the lights on.

"Can't… hic…" was the drunken reply from another long haired beauty, "this is all the light we got." Our patient was found in a drunken state leaning against a makeshift partition that separated what looked like a large ground floor flat. She had stab wounds to both arms and one shoulder but it took a lot to persuade her to come with us to hospital for treatment. In the end she agreed, but only if three of her mates could come with her. We said that would be OK, provided they all behaved themselves whilst onboard the ambulance and at the casualty department.

Aboard *Richmond Three*, John helped me dress the patient's wounds before jumping behind the wheel to take us to St Stephen's Hospital.

"Don't want the police involved," the patient said to me as we pulled away.

I nodded my reply, thinking to myself, 'something's not right – I can't put my finger on it, but something is not right.'

It was only when we were at the casualty department that the penny dropped. John and I were standing in the reception area talking to the sister when the three beauties stood up, turned and marched off in line to the toilets, watched by all who were sitting around and waiting their turn to be seen. The three marched straight into the 'gents'. They were transvestites, which explained the rather deep voice of one of the 'passengers' in the back of the ambulance and the five o'clock shadow on one of the 'girls' – other than that they were incredibly convincing – unbelievable but true. Everybody in the reception area stared at the toilet door, waiting for their return, with which we were all blessed after a few minutes wait. All three, again in line, sashayed across the floor, showing off their false assets to the spellbound onlookers before taking their seats and striking up an animated conversation in high-pitched voices, mingled with female giggling.

We were still shaking our heads in disbelief as we turned out of the hospital when we were directed to a high class night club-cum-casino in Cromwell Road, West Kensington, where a female had collapsed and was believed to be unconscious.

We found our patient, a young girl of seventeen, lying on her back in the toilets on the ground floor surrounded by a crowd of her friends, not one of whom knew what to do whilst waiting for our arrival. Her airways were full of stale vomit and no life signs were present. We spent the next twenty five minutes carrying out the full resuscitation procedures before deciding to make a run back to St Stephens casualty with a blue call placed with Red Base. A few minutes after our arrival she was certified dead in the back of the ambulance. Another terrible waste. If we had only been called ten or even five minutes earlier, who knows, we might have saved her.

We received another call over the R/T as we neared our own patch on the way back to Richmond after our last few hectic hours in West London. It was a call to assist *Richmond One* and *Putney One*, who were in attending an RTA at Barnes Common, where a mini car had left the road and crashed into a tree. The scene was illuminated by many blue lights as we neared the accident site. One female had already been removed from the site before our arrival and the *Putney One* crew were in the act of removing a fatality from the wreckage. It turned out to be the pop star, Marc Bolan. With a little help from us at the scene, the lead singer of T-Rex was removed to Queen Mary's Hospital by the *Putney One* crew and we returned, very tired, to our own station.

Two other calls come to mind from the last weeks that I worked out of Richmond with Johnny Marsh. The first was to end successfully, the second involved the tragic loss of a man who had become a friend to the pair of us.

We had just pulled out of New Malden ambulance station following a vehicle change and were on our way back to Richmond when Red Base called, requesting our position over the R/T, which I gave as approaching the junction of Cambridge Road and Gloucester Road. The call was to an address in Hampden Road, Kingston, where the caller had reported that a baby had stopped breathing. It just so happened, John had parked *Richmond One* whilst I took the call down, a few yards from the junction of Hampden Road, so we were outside the address in a matter of seconds. A ten-month-old baby girl had been found lying face down in a pram that had been filled up with water by the little girl's four-year-old brother, using a hosepipe. Running up the path we were met by two hysterical women screaming their heads off, one of whom forcefully grabbed my arm and pulled me towards the swamped baby carriage.

Without a second thought, I grabbed the baby by the ankles and held it upside down. The water poured from it's mouth and down the front of my shirt and trousers. Upending the cyanosed infant, I sat down on a nearby bench and started mouth/nose resuscitation as the two women behind me ran around in circles screaming, "Do something ... Do something please!" The infant coughed and sputtered more water from the airways and I noticed with relief that the blue tinge was quickly disappearing. The baby was soon breathing unassisted, and with two big blue eyes starring up at me, she burst into a loud coughing cry. With a nod to John, I placed the little girl in his outstretched arms and he made his way back down the path to the waiting ambulance. I held both women's hands and led them down to the rear of the ambulance, where they could see for themselves John stripping off the wet romper suit and placing the crying infant in a warm blanket.

Instantly, the two women were silenced by what they saw. One, the mother, climbed aboard to be near her child. Leaving John in the back, I climbed in the driving seat and after a minute we were pulling up outside Kingston casualty department.

Outside the department a little while later, whilst John and I were enjoying a cigarette, the mother joined us. Full of emotion, she tearfully embraced each of us in turn, thanking us for what we had done and assuring us that we would be remembered for the rest of her life. The baby, we were told later, made a full recovery and returned home after a

48-hour hospital stay. (I often wondered what the outcome would have been if we hadn't, by chance, been so close when called to the emergency).

Richard Johnson was a double amputee and an asthmatic, who nevertheless enjoyed his Golden Virginia 'roll-up' cigarettes. He was quite a character, forever spinning yarns that seemed to change in content every time John and I picked him up for his clinic appointments when were working *Richmond Five* daytime shifts on 'white' non-emergency work. Richard had become a good friend to us and it was always a pleasure to have him onboard when his trips were due.

John and I were relaxing on station late one evening shortly before we were due to be relieved by the on-coming night crew when the bells went off, the call-out being to a house fire in the Mortlake area, where persons had been reported trapped.

As we ran to the ambulance I turned to John and said, "I know that address, it rings a bell."

"Me too," he answered.

I pushed our ambulance at speed along Upper Richmond Road with the two tones blaring and blue lights flashing. After crossing the railway at Sheen, we turned into Mortlake High Street. The turning we were looking for was the next on the right…

"Oh fuck!" I said aloud, as we entered the dead-end street.

It was Richard Johnson's house that the firemen were playing their hoses on.

My heart leapt into my mouth.

After parking our vehicle in position for a quick getaway, if needed, I opened the rear doors and walked down the pavement to join my colleague. We stood watching as the firefighters entered the premises for he first time. It seemed a lifetime waiting for them to re-emerge and report their findings to the white-helmeted officer. The whole of the ground floor had been severely damaged, and a body had been found in the kitchen, well beyond medical aid.

After a short time, the fire officer led us round to the back of the building, where we entered the burnt-out kitchen through the still smouldering back door that had been wrenched off it's hinges.

In the kitchen that we had been in so many times before, in the corner beside the Victorian fireplace, were the unrecognisable remains of our friend, in the burnt out shell of his wheelchair.

I prayed that his end had come quickly and painlessly.

Richard was removed from the fire-damaged house by the undertakers a few hours after the scene-of-crime officers had finished their investigations into the cause of the fire. He was buried a week later at Hammersmith Cemetery, the service attended by the many friends that this likable man had made over the years – a true gentleman.

It was reported in the local press that the probable cause of the fire was that Richard had dropped a can of lighter fluid into his lap whilst filling his lighter and smoking at the same time. Either ash or his cigarette must have fallen into his lap, igniting the fluid.

My couple of years working New Malden, Tolworth, and Richmond ambulance stations were now coming to an end. I had received instructions to report to Streatham ambulance station the following Monday. I was going to miss the lads – I had made many good friends – but the move was going to benefit me greatly with regard to the time I spent travelling. It was a transfer I hoped I wasn't going to regret. After a pleasant evening spent with John and the off-duty crews at the Kings Arms in Richmond, I said my final farewells.

PART V

Streatham – The Oval and Paramedic Training

Streatham is a small, two-vehicle accident and emergency station, which had been built around 1920 and was very similar layout to the training station I had worked in at Bloomsbury. The catchment area was large, covering a population of nearly 125 thousand – with Brixton to the north, Mitcham to the south, Tooting to the west and Crystal Palace eastwards, with the result that Streatham was a very busy accident station, with each crew attending, on average, six emergency calls per shift. Like Richmond, one ambulance was on cover for 24-hours, the second vehicle covering from seven o'clock in the morning until eleven o'clock at night with the opportunity for the late-turn crew to work until the early hours if requested by control when the workload warranted it.

For me, it was a blessing to live only a ten-minute drive away from work after my years of making the tiring daily round-trip to and from Richmond.

My first two days at Streatham were spent going out with the duty crews to familiarise myself with the area and the station routines (which vary a little from station to station). My first shift on the rota was the late-turn week commencing on a Wednesday afternoon on *Streatham Three*. I was to be crewed with the oldest serving ambulanceman at the station, Doug Terry, an experienced 52-year-old. My first call-out with Doug from Streatham on that Wednesday afternoon was to a row of garages off Bedford Hill in Balham, where a street-wise 16-year-old prostitute had been assaulted by an early afternoon punter, her third of the day.

"Hi Sally, let's have a look," Doug said, bending down to inspect the inflicted damage.

Her face was a swollen blue and red mess, with one eye completely closed and the other a mere slit with tears rolling down the bruised cheek.

"I know the bastard. I'll have his bollocks next time I see him!" she said, tilting her head back to allow Doug to treat, as best he could, the ever-increasing swelling.

"He got me money... What's me mum going to say?"

"Quiet now... one thing at a time... let's get you sorted out before worrying about that," Doug cajoled, as he applied a wet dressing pad to her rapidly-changing facial features.

At St James Hospital casualty department we settled Sally into a cubicle before returning to Streatham Three.

Once outside the department I asked, "Do you know Sally then Doug?"

"I know all her family – known them for years. All the same, on the game, four of them, mother, and three daughters. They never learn. We're always being called out to them – either bashed up by some punter, or an overdose of whatever they can get hold off, or like most weekends found drunk in Balham High Road after doing a tour of the local pubs looking for anything in trousers. You'll get used to them," he said, smiling.

My first day at Streatham came to a close after a busy shift. Following Sally's call, we had two collapse cases, one suspected heart attack, one epileptic fit of a teenager on a train, an RTA with two casualties and, to end the day, a hospital admission to St Georges Hospital Tooting, with an elderly female suffering with a CVA (stroke).

My first few months at Streatham flew past, and I quickly fell into my new station routines. It helped a lot that I was working with different crew-members over this initial period. I was now learning the back-street short-cuts around the patch to shorten the running time to calls, and was getting to know, on first name terms, the casualty staff at the four main hospitals in our area.

After one of the station crew-members left the service to become an estate agent, several of us moved around on the rosters to crew-up with a different colleague. I crewed with Laurie Low, the stepson of the station officer at the Oval, Mr Churcher.

Laurie and I were to work together for the next couple of years, and it was to become another great working and socialising relationship along the lines of my time spent at Richmond with Johnny Marsh. Laurie had a great sense of humour, which helped in the stresses that faced us daily as events unfolded. He was also very methodical in his assessment and treatment of patients and an understanding and trust soon built up between us as we battled through our ever-increasing workload.

Grown men do cry. I for one admit it without embarrassment. It can be a great relief if feelings are allowed to release themselves following a tragic event, especially when children are involved.

Three such events come to mind from the time that Laurie and I were crewed together.

The first was a fire at a house in Franciscan Road, Tooting. The fire brigade were already on scene as we pulled up close to the fire tenders in the ambulance.

"Got three kids in there," the white-helmeted fire officer greeted us with, as we looked up at the smoke and flames spewing from the top-floor windows. The three young children had been left alone in the house whilst the mother had gone to an all-night party, leaving the children to fend for themselves. The youngsters had started a fire in a back bedroom and in no time at all it had taken hold, denying them any means of escape. I requested that Red Base send another ambulance to scene, as further casualties were expected.

We stood, watching and waiting, while firemen did their best in attempting a rescue. Our waiting was rewarded when a fireman in breathing apparatus appeared from the smoking hallway with a child in his arms. Taking the child from the fireman, I placed him straight on the pavement, where Laurie and I started resuscitation procedures, illuminated by floodlight beams from the nearby fire engines. It was a hopeless task. The child was to hot to physically touch and was obviously beyond medical aid, but we continued until a second child was brought out and placed on the pavement. This time medical aid was impossible, the upper body was so severely burnt that resuscitation could not be carried out.

The second ambulance to scene was *Wimbledon One*. We were helping load the two children onboard their vehicle when Laurie and I were called by the fire officer and told that a third child, now being removed from the building, was still breathing. I ran with the child in my arms to the ambulance, where Laurie was waiting with aspirator at the ready, oxygen lines in place and the green resui-bag prepared for the forthcoming attempt if the young girl should arrest on us. We worked for next five minutes in the back of the ambulance as an audience of fire and police officers watched us. We aspirated, inserted an airway and attached the air lines to the resuscitation bag as we assisted the laboured breathing from the young smoke filled lungs.

"Can you close the doors for us, were going to make a run for it in a tick," I said, without looking up.

"Yeah mate," came the reply, as the doors closed with a bang. A young woman police officer had climbed on board and was going to escort us on the fast run to St Georges. I heard Laurie place a blue call, followed by his firing the engine and felt the bumps as we pulled away forward over the charged fire hoses. We had only gone a few hundred yards when I lost the monitored pulse – the child had arrested.

"Go! Go Laurie, she's arrested!" I shouted above the din of the two-tones.

"Can you do closed chest cardiac massage while I use the bag?" I asked the young police officer.

"I'll have a go," she said, moving her position to the side of the trolley bed in the swaying vehicle.

"Am I doing alright?" the officer asked a couple of times.

"You're doing OK, you're doing it just right," I assured her as she pumped away as I squeezed the green bag, inflating the child's damaged lungs at the required rate.

In the crash room at St Georges, resuscitation attempts continued for thirty five minutes before a reluctant decision to discontinue was made by the senior paediatrician and the girl was wheeled over to join her blanket-covered siblings in the corner of the room.

Three children – a nine year old girl, her six year old sister and their five year old brother had lost their lives that night, because of an accident while playing with matches, but mainly because of their neglect by an irresponsible partygoer.

Tear-streaked sooty faces stared back from the mirrored walls that night as ambulance and police officers cleaned up in the casualty department toilets together in silence, keeping their thoughts to themselves, but sharing the tear-filled experience.

The second event took place during the rush hour one evening on the outskirts of Streatham.

We received a call to an RTA that had occurred in Mitcham Lane, and were informed that a child had been injured; the young girl involved had been knocked down by a car whilst using a pedestrian crossing. She was on her way to a brownies meeting, just a few hundred yards from her home. She was unconscious when we arrived and had received multiple injuries, including an obvious skull fracture. Both eyes were fixed and dilated with no reaction; she was in a sorry state. With an airway inserted and her breathing assisted with the resuscitation bag, we moved her to the ambulance. Following a blue call to Red Base, we travelled at high speed through the heavy rush hour traffic to St George's hospital at Tooting. The nine-year-old died fifteen minutes later despite the desperate efforts of the crash room staff who did their utmost to stabilise her condition. A terrible loss, due, we later learned, to a driver who had been drinking for several hours prior to using his untaxed car on that tragic journey through Mitcham on a warm summer's evening.

A third event involving a child that always comes to mind, was a call to a restaurant in West Norwood, where the owner's child, a little chap of five, had wandered into the kitchen area, climbed on a stool and placed his right hand into a commercial self-starting mincer. His injury was obviously horrific. We had to unbolt the machine from the table before we could remove the boy, with mincer still attached, and rush him to the casualty department at King's College Hospital.

In the majority of 'accidents' involving minors – and the three cases mentioned above are just a few of those I have attended – the youngsters always seem to suffer, or worse still, lose their lives, not so much because of their own childish curiosity, but as a result of negligence by so-called 'grown-ups' whose job it should be to protect the young from harm.

Fortunately, ambulance work can also have its unexpectedly humorous moments – even in potentially life-threatening situations… The following incident occurred during a period when the London Fire Brigade were taking industrial action over their pay and conditions, leaving fire calls in the Capital to be covered by military personnel aboard their 'Green Goddess' fire engines, which were stationed mainly at police stations where the 999 calls for their attendance were diverted. At this time all London's front line ambulances carried an extra fire extinguisher to deal with (very small) fires, if we should be first on the scene.

Late one afternoon, Laurie and I were on our way back from King's College Hospital when we were waved down by a passing motorist, who told us breathlessly that there was a fire a little further up the road. Laurie informed control over the R/T as I pushed *Streatham One* at speed towards the reported incident. Just a minute later, I pulled the vehicle to a standstill outside a five-storey building that had smoke billowing out of the ground floor windows.

"Oh, fuck!" we said together, as we climbed down from the ambulance.

An old man with a dog in his arms was coming down the front steps as we made our first approach towards the open front door.

"You alright old timer?" Laurie asked, as he took the old man's arm to guide him down the last steps.

"Yeah mate, we're alright," he said, squeezing his dog to his chest. "It's my kitchen mate... I fell asleep and forgot the chip pan. The dog woke me, barking like mad, bless her heart!" He kisse the top of the bewildered dog's head.

"Anyone else in the building?" Laurie asked, looking around at the smoke that was getting thicker by the minute.

Shuffling his feet in his well-worn slippers the old man replied, "nah, they're out all day... 'cept the girl on the top floor – she works at night and kips in the afternoon, I fink."

"Jesus Christ! – Right... you stay here, and tell any police or firemen that turn up, that we have gone inside, understand?" Laurie instructed the old man.

"Yeah mate, I'll do that," the old man replied, and sat down on the lower steps.

Armed with a crowbar and a hammer, Laurie and I quickly entered the building and in great haste climbed the five flights of stairs, banging on doors as we went up, until we were faced with a big oak door leading to the top flat. After thumping loudly on the door and receiving no response from within, we decided to attempt to force an entry as wisps of smoke started to rise from the staircase below.

With an almighty crunch, the door gave way to our efforts and we entered the large flat, shouting as we went from room to room, Laurie eventually coming to the bedroom. I found him gazing open-mouthed at an empty unmade bed; scanty female clothing was scattered around the floor and a very large collection of female sexual aids adorned the large dressing table in front of the curtained windows.

"Let's get going John… nothing here," he said, with a broad grin.

On our descent down the staircase we met with ever-increasing black smoke and we were both coughing and spluttering as we reached the open air back at street level.

The police arrived shortly afterwards, with a crew of Royal Navy fire-fighters aboard their 'Green Goddess', who took about an hour to get the fire under control, leaving two floors burnt out with the remainder of the building smoke-damaged.

The old man and his dog were catered for by the local council.

About a week later, Mr Churcher, Laurie's father, turned up on station. We were due for a telling off, he told us. The service had received a bill from the occupant of the flat we had broken into on the fire call at Norwood. Her claim was for the replacement of the oak door and surround, totalling three hundred pounds, and she also thought it unnecessary that we had to gain entry.

'There is no pleasing some people, whatever the situation,' we thought. But perhaps it was more of an embarrassment to her that we had witnessed her 'playthings' in the bedroom than anything else we had done that day.

The months rolled by at Streatham, each day as busy as the last. There were a couple of domestic-related murders, and we received more and more calls to attend serious assaults where knives, and in some cases, firearms had been used. It was a daily event to treat mugging victims and the local working girls who walked the common at Tooting Bec, whose dangerous occupation left them open to attack.

The time eventually came for Laurie and I to end our working relationship. He was moved to the Oval main station to take over as acting L.A.M. due to a long-term sickness vacancy. As for myself, I received the news that I had been accepted for paramedic training at headquarters.

The social life of the Streatham crews around this time was great. Monthly get-togethers with wives and girlfriends had become a regular event and we were taking it in turns to host the parties or outings, one of which was a memorable evening at a nightclub in Essex, where comedian Mike Reed topped the bill.

Entering the training school at Headquarters again after such a long time felt strange, and the old nervousness returned as I took my place alongside the other eleven students who had been selected for 'Advanced Training Course No.19'. The two training officers, along with a doctor, introduced themselves and then informally presented the forthcoming program for the course. A mixture of lectures, instructions on the use of drugs, advanced resuscitation procedures, practical work involving the art of intubation and infusion, and written examinations were to take up the time whilst we were at the training school for the next four weeks. If successful, this was to be followed by at least a three-week period working under the instructions of an anaesthetist in an operating theatre and casualty department.

The following weeks were very informative, week one covering the subject of chest injuries and diseases, respiratory failure and it's conditions and treatment.

Week two, and more on the subject of respiratory distress, followed by practical sessions of how and when to intubate a casualty. The week ended with an open question and answer period followed by a written examination.

Week three was taken up completely by the subject of the cardiovascular system – it's make up, the signs and symptoms of the various types of heart failure, the treatments to be administered, the use of the blood pressure cuff and stethoscope, practical instruction on how to set up intravenous infusion lines, the Hartman's and Haemocell fluids used and how to gauge the flow rates required for various medical con-

Students of Advanced Training Course No. 19 along with the two instructors and Dr Gardner, the London Ambulance Service doctor.

ditions. The week ended with another written examination and a one-to-one talk with the ambulance service doctor.

The final week at the training school arrived and the next two days were taken up solely with the subject of head injuries and their treatment.

Wednesday was revision day and on Thursday examination day arrived.

The morning taken up with practical tests. We each took turns at intubating a manikin several times, to the satisfaction of the on looking instructor, this was followed by the setting up of an infusion line and running the fluid at a requested rate into the veins of a dummy arm.

Lunch was spent amongst a new intake of students to the service and my thoughts returned to my first few days in the building five years ago, wondering, as no-doubt some of them were, whether I had made the right career choice. I had to smile as I looked around the smoke-filled room.

My own nervousness returned as I made my decent to the ground floor classroom to join my colleagues sitting at their desks waiting for the final written paper, which duly arrived with the instruction that we had one and a half hours to complete it, and that no talking amongst the seated twelve would be permitted.

With the exam over, the twelve of us made our way to the canteen for well earned tea and cigarettes in the over-crowded lounge. On our return to the lower floor, a little later, we were greeted by an instructor.

"Have a good evening… See you all back here sharp at nine o'clock tomorrow morning when you will be told of your results," was all he said as he left the room, leaving us disappointed. We had hoped for some indication as to the outcome of our efforts.

Friday morning eventually arrived after a long and restless night.

"Good morning all – please take your seats," was the welcome as the two instructors and the doctor entered the classroom and stood before us.

"First, congratulations are in order, you all passed with flying colours!"

Enthusiastic whooping and cheering broke out and wide grins appeared on the faces of the trio standing before us. In the course of the following hour, the instructors informed us individually which hospital we would be working at, and the set procedures we must adhere to whilst working under the instruction of operating staff in the theatre suites.

I was to report, along with John Palmer, another student on the following Monday morning at eight o'clock to the theatre sister at the Brook Hospital, Woolwich where we would be working with anaesthetists Doctor Lobo, Doctor Silver and Doctor De-Mitre. A weekly report would be furnished by each of the doctors to ambulance headquarters, stating our progress leading to a final assessment at the end of the full training period.

I found my time spent 'below ground' in the operating theatres at the Brook Hospital over the following three week period, very rewarding. I was very fortunate in that the three anaesthetists I had the pleasure of working with were very helpful and instructive during my period there. With the surgery starting sharp at nine o'clock each morning, I was dressed in 'greens' and ready to accompany my tutor to the theatre ante-room to prepare each incoming patient for surgery in the adjoining suite. Under instruction, I quickly learnt the art of inserting butterfly needles ready for the intravenous supply of drugs required for the forthcoming operation and went on to be taught about the setting up and running of drip feed sets, using a face mask along with the Boyle's anaesthetic machine and finally the specialised art of intubation – inserting a tube through the vocal cords that are stretched across the larynx and into the trachea space leading to the lungs.

The intubations I carried out varied from patient to patient. Some I found quite easy, but with others – those with a small mouth or large protruding front teeth – I found it very difficult at first to manipulate the laryngoscope inside the mouth. However, with the large amount of patients passing through the theatres over the weeks and the consequent amount of practise, I found the action becoming a lot easier to carry out.

I found it fascinating to watch the surgeons and their teams going about their business – the nuro-surgeon was a massive man with large hands, but delicate in his work; the orthopaedic surgeon with his 'workshop' of tools for carrying out hip replacements and the thoracic surgeon working away inside the chest cavity.

"You won't learn anything standing over there … come and have a closer look," he would say on many occasions when I was in his theatre.

Twice I was asked to accompany an anaesthetist to the casualty department on the ground floor to attend an unconscious patient who had been brought in by ambulance and required intubating and ventilating. Once we were called to the coronary care unit for an elderly lady who had suffered a cardiac arrest. After being intubated and resuscitated, she survived to live another day.

I was instructed to return to Waterloo Headquarters at nine o'clock on the Friday morning of my final week of hospital training, so with handshakes and wishes of good luck from the operating theatre staff I left the Brook Hospital for the last time on the Thursday evening.

I was informed on the Friday that I had passed my advanced aid training course and was now a Paramedic with the service. After an informal interview with the service doctor, I was issued with my own personal fully-stocked intubation and infusion kit, that had to be carried with me at all times I was on duty. Following a de-brief of the hospital training and a few more handshakes, we twelve new paramedics left headquarters on that afternoon, very proud, and looking forward to the new challenges that awaited us on the road.

At home , my wife Jackie opened the front door to find a grinning husband standing before her with boxes in hand.

"You done it?" she asked hugging me.

"Yup, I did it," I replied stepping proudly inside, taking the kit into the lounge, where over next hour I explained the workings of the contents of each box in turn, ending by telling her of the morning's events at headquarters with the doctor and instructors. That evening, Jackie and I celebrated with a meal, followed by a night out on the town, where for the first time in seven weeks I really felt relaxed and sociable. I was looking forward to the next five days off duty before returning to crew *Streatham Three India* (India denotes a paramedic crew) the following Wednesday with a new colleague and my own advanced aid medical kit.

Mark Cullis was my new crewmate, a spectacled, fresh-faced thirty-year-old who had been with the service for the last three years. He was a good driver, very ambitious and was shortly to be accepted for his paramedic training. Our first weeks working together were very quiet by Streatham standards and the first time my advanced aid skills were called for was as we were returning to base from a hoax call when the R/T burst into life.

"Streatham One India Report, Over."

"Denmark Hill Approaching Herne Hill Station, Over," I replied.

"Roger Streatham, Call Red Accident for you when you're ready, Over."

"Go Ahead."

"It's A Call Red Accident to outside Number 30, Tulse Hill, South West Two, where a male has collapsed on the top deck of a number two bus – Police in attendance – timed to you at 1613 hours – Mike Bravo, Streatham One India, Over."

I read the call back to the controller as Mark switched on the warning devices and headed our Vehicle at speed along the perimeter of Brockwell Park leading to the busy Tulse Hill area.

My patient, an elderly male, was conscious as I arrived on the top deck of the bus to join the police officer.

"Hello mate – ambulance service – have you got any pains anywhere?" I asked, bending down to look into his glazed eyes, whilst at the same time avoiding his vomit-covered trousers.

Without answering, he slowly raised his hand to point towards his chest area with blue-tinged fingers.

"Chair, blanket and oxygen please Mark," I said to my colleague as he joined me on the upper deck.

"Do you want me to clear the bus for yer mate?" a worried looking conductor asked.

"Good idea, save any embarrassment, plus this will need clearing up," I said nodding towards the pool of evil-smelling vomit beneath the seat.

Mark returned with the equipment as the last of the passengers had descended the spiral staircase, leaving us alone with the policeman to carry out the removal. With a gasp from beneath the attached oxygen mask, the patient's head fell forward as we were preparing to move him across to the carrying chair.

"Shit, he's gone," I said, as I lifted his chin to inspect his glazed and fixed dilated pupils.

"A little bit of KY gel on a ten point five tube Mark," I asked for the first time as I manoeuvred the laryngoscope around the pharynx of a sitting patient. Sighting the vocal cords, illuminated by the mini-bulb, I held out my hand for the Portex curved tube, and then carefully intubated the elderly gentlemen. With the air cuff inflated by the attached syringe I tied off the top of the tube to prevent it moving, and with the oxygen assisted ventilating bag started the resuscitation procedure as we laid him down on the well-trodden floor.

"Hold on a tick," I said aloud, after working on him for about five minutes, "I can feel a feeble pulse in his carotid." A few more seconds passed as I monitored the output with my fingers aside his neck.

"Yup, it's there – Come on, let's make a move for the ambulance," I said with some excitement.

With a blue call placed with Red Base, Mark eased *Streatham Three India* out into early evening traffic for a fast blue light run through Brixton, on towards Camberwell as I struggled in the back of the swaying ambulance until Mark pulled us in to the ambulance bay at Kings College.

Fifty minutes later, after two successful resuscitation attempts following cardiac arrests in the crash room, the doctor leading the team decided after the third arrest that the present attempt, which was not resulting in any output, should be aborted and our patient was certified life expired.

"Well done lads, a good tube job – it was worth a try, but it wasn't to be I'm afraid," the doctor said as he joined us for coffee in the staff room.

My journey back to Streatham was tinged with a little sadness. I had hoped for a better result, especially after obtaining a cardiac output on board the bus. However, I was to learn over the coming months, as my newly-learnt intubation procedures were called for in ever-increasing numbers, that the chances for recovery were far better than the standard re-sus-bag attempts I had carried out prior to my advanced training. It was a great feeling to know that several of my intubated patients had at least made it to the coronary or intensive care units via the casualty department to live another day – and in a couple that I know of, to be discharged following a full recovery.

The first time I put my infusion gear to use, was a cold and wet miserable night in south London. We were called to a top floor flat in the heart of Balham, where a four-month pregnant woman had collapsed in a bathroom following a severe post-vaginal blood loss. With the blood pressure readings showing a rapid drop, indicating further internal haemorrhaging, I decided to infuse with a unit of Hartman's as quickly as possible. Finding a suitable site to insert the cannula was another problem, the veins were untraceable, and it took a second attempt before the needle back flowed with the dark coloured liquid. The first two hundred and fifty millilitres I ran in very fast, followed by the second set to run at about forty drips a minute. With a rise in the pressure readings, the time had come to carry out the removal, and very slowly, after making the embarrassed naked female comfortable, we started the slow decent down to the ambulance, followed by a steady journey on to St Georges Hospital at Tooting.

I was to carry out many more infusions whilst working out of Streatham, most were to road accident victims, a few to factory or building site accident casualties and a few cardiac cases.

Laurie Low, my earlier crewmate had been offered a position at Headquarters in the control Room, and because of his acceptance, I was offered the job of covering the long-term sickness vacancy of the leading ambulanceman at the Oval Main ambulance station, a position I accepted.

The duties consisted of a four shift system around the clock, covering all aspects of paperwork from the emergency and day turn crews, arranging cover for sickness and annual leave, insuring stock levels were maintained at the Oval and Streatham and, last of all, arranging vehicle changes for maintenance at the workshops at Brixton. At about four thirty each afternoon the station was vacated by the Senior Officer and his assistant, leaving the L.A.M. to run the main and satellite stations on his own. I found the challenge quite exiting when left alone in charge for the first time, and with the silver bar attached to my epaulettes I settled down at my desk for the task in hand.

One Saturday afternoon whist doing some paperwork, Red Base rung me to ask if I was paramedic trained.

"Yes," I replied.

"Good – We will be putting you to more use from now on, starting today." With that statement, I was sent out on my first call as a Leading Ambulanceman with the call sign for my staff car being *Oval Oscar Three*. The call was to assist a Waterloo crew at an RTA where two of the casualties required infusions to overcome severe blood loss whilst trapped in an overturned car.

Several times in the coming weeks my skills were put to the test as I turned out in the staff car *Oval Oscar Three* to serious incidents at various locations in south London.

I assisted another paramedic when called late one evening to an RTA near Lewisham High Road, where two young male casualties required intubation and fluid replacement following their removal from an upturned car that had caught fire. Both youngsters, I later learned, survived the follow-up treatment at the accident and emergency department of Lewisham Hospital, but were to face many months of painful skin grafts at a well-known south London burns unit.

It was around this time that the unrest between the West Indian community and the Metropolitan Police in the Brixton area occurred, leading to the infamous riots causing millions of pounds worth of property damage in an area of approximately one square mile. All service leave leading up to this dreadful weekend was cancelled as emergency plans were put into place.

I was on my way to the area in *Oval Oscar Three* when I was called by many shouts to the market area of Brixton, where I witnessed scenes that had not been seen in the Capital since the war years. Rows of shops, public houses, cars, and private premises were ablaze. All the emergency service personnel in the area were coming under a barrage of missiles being thrown by angry mobs that had gathered on the smoke shrouded street corners. In the quieter back streets, teams of nervous-looking St John's Ambulance workers at first aid posts were busy treating the minor injuries that had been sent to them. More serious casualties, who required more medical expertise, were being transferred to hospital by the service vehicles. I carried out many trips to and from the local hospital casualty departments, intubated two head injury patients and infused a couple of rioters who had received serious leg injuries after falling across shards of glass whilst climbing out of a broken shop window whilst looting a well-known high street electrical store.

It was a very long and stressful weekend, one I shall never forget and it was a pitiful sight to see the burnt out buildings and the damage caused to the surrounding area when I passed through Brixton a few days later after some form of normality had returned to the stunned community.

My leading ambulanceman duties were to come to an end after fourteen months at the Oval Main station. The long-term sickness vacancy was to cease as the passed-fit L.A.M. would be resuming his duties very shortly, I was advised early one morning.

I had enjoyed the time spent at the main station, the challenge, the office work, the occasional callouts to serious incidents where I had the opportunity to put my advanced aid skills to use, and most of all, working alongside the other LAMs and station staff who had been more than helpful to me since the earliest days when I first arrived amongst them.

I was now prepared to return to Streatham, and to resume the accident shifts back on the front line aboard, *Streatham One, and Three.*

Mark, my crewmate, had passed his advanced aid course whilst I was away and we were one of the first teams in the service to crew an accident and emergency vehicle with two paramedics.

I soon picked up the swing of things as I returned to the day to day routine of the station, and it was a pleasure to be back in the action as the calls came in thick and fast.

Mark and I had been selected as a crew by headquarters, to man a front-line vehicle solely for the use of the Pope on his visit for three days to the Capital. It was an interesting time, as we were briefed by police and security department staff what to do in the event of a terrorist attack on his Holiness, or the removal arrangements if he had the misfortune to be taken ill anytime he was in London. The Pontiff's visit to the Capital went smoothly, however. We followed him around in our ambulance – call-sign *Papal One* – during his busy schedule, but thankfully without any need for medical attention from us or the other paramedic crews who worked round the clock. We had been told that his Holiness was suffering with a chest infection and had been pumped full of antibiotics by his personal physician, but all went well. Another experience never to be forgotten.

In the long hot summer that followed, Jackie and I took young Stephen on holiday to the Isle-of- Wight, where we enjoyed ourselves at a caravan park close to the sandy beaches of Whitecliff Bay. Lazy days were spent swimming and sunbathing, followed by music-filled evenings at the site's nightclub. It was nice to get away from both our stress-filled occupations, albeit for just a couple of weeks. It was here that we decided it was time to made a break from our busy lifestyle and move away from London, and where better, than the Isle-of-Wight?. Two days before our holiday was due to come to an end, we spotted a small, two-bedroomed cottage for sale on the outskirts of Bembridge, a mile from the sea. The owners, a pleasant middle-aged couple, must have seen us admiring their little domain, so much so they invited us to look over the property, which was very neatly laid out and included a well-stocked and maintained sixty foot garden backing onto farmland. We fell in love with it straight away, and, knowing we would have little trouble in selling our house in London, we exchanged details, promising to make contact on return to the Capital.

We sold our house within a few hours of it going on the market, and our offer for the cottage at Bembridge was accepted subject to the normal conditions. Back at work, I put in a transfer request to the Isle- of-Wight Ambulance Service and sat back and waited for a favourable reply.

Six weeks to the day had passed from when we first saw the cottage, and with a lot of help from two of my work colleagues, Mark Cullis and Mick Boyland, we made our move from the Smoke to the peace and quiet of the beautiful island.

I soon got into the routine of working five weeks on the trot at Streatham, followed by a week off duty at home on the Island. I had the good fortune to be offered a room at Micky Boyland's house near Tooting during my tours of duty on the mainland, with Mick and his family making me more than welcome, but it was great as each five-week period came to an end to take the main A3 road out of town and head for Old Portsmouth and the Isle-of-Wight car ferry, which took me home to our cottage by the sea.

Jackie and I had settled into the country way of life quite quickly, and soon made a circle of friends from nearby Bembridge village, who ensured that my wife was safe and secure whilst I was working away on the mainland. To this day we still socialise with the same crowd from those early days when we first set foot on their island.

Back at Streatham it was as busy as ever. Three railway accidents occurred over a period of a few days. The first was a call to Clapham South underground station, where a woman had fallen in the path of an incoming northbound tube train.

Easing down between the carriages, we slowly moved across the running rails and dropped into the pit beneath the train. The patient, a middle-aged, well-dressed woman was still alive but unconscious. She had suffered severe head injuries and had lost her left leg. Her left arm was almost severed at the elbow and beneath her torn fur coat a pneumothorax was very evident as she was already in respiratory distress. With the help of my grease-covered colleague, we managed to seal the air-sucking wound in the chest wall and intubate her with a twelve point five Portex tube. It was only after the tube train had been pulled clear and she had been lifted to the now clear platform that we were able to infuse her with fast flowing Haemocell fluid.

The unfortunate lady lost her fight for life several hours later whilst on her second visit to the operating theatre at St James's Hospital in Balham. At least the joint efforts of the rescue crews and the opportunity given to me to administer advanced medical aid at scene had given the woman a chance of survival, albeit a slim one.

The second railway accident was the following evening, when we were called to Norwood Junction station, where a male had been found trackside after being struck by a passing high speed train. Our recovery of the beyond-aid naked victim was very time consuming, as the body parts were spread over a wide area, the very gruesome task made worse by torrential rain.

The following Sunday lunchtime we received over the R/T, our third railway incident of the week, and it was rather poignant for me because of my previous occupation. This casualty turned out to be a railway worker.

"Streatham One India please report," the radio burst into life.

"Tooting Bec Common," I replied.

"Call Red Accident, if you're ready, Over."

"Roger – Go Ahead."

"Thank you Streatham, it's a Call Red accident to a railway bridge flyover beside Streatham Common Signal Box. A member of staff has been electrocuted and is unconscious – Timed at 1223 fours, Delta Foxtrot, Streatham One India, Over."

I read the call back to the controller as Micky Boyland, my crewmate for the day, steered the ambulance at high speed towards our target.

The patient, a nineteen-year-old railway painter, had fallen from a ladder whilst painting a section of the flyover bridge and had landed across the running and conductor rails, where his metal neck chain had made a short circuit causing severe burning to his throat which led to the blockage of his airway. He was beyond aid when we arrived, his eyes fixed and fully dilated, with no life signs present. At first, his colleagues couldn't understand why we were unable to even attempt resuscitation on the young man, until, by using the laryngoscope, I actually showed the man in charge the damage that had been caused to the victim's pharynx cavity.

With the help of the fire service, using ropes and a Neil Robertson stretcher, it took nearly half an hour to remove the young victim from trackside to our waiting ambulance, and with the railway ganger and a police inspector on board we made the solemn journey to St James Hospital where, after the lad was examined and certified by the duty doctor, Mick and myself removed him to the coldness of the Purple Annex.

Saturday 17th October 1981 was a day that was truly memorable. I was on early turn and was looking forward to finishing my shift and starting my journey home to join my wife on the island for the next five days. Bliss – sheer bliss. At 11.34 the emergency phone at Streatham jangled into life.

The call was to a 'query explosion / query RTA' at South Croxted Road, Dulwich SE21.

Both *Streatham One India* and *Streatham Three India*, along with a visiting day crew, were dispatched to scene, and within a few seconds all three vehicles were speeding towards the Dulwich district a couple of miles away. A very strong smell of explosives hung in the dust-filled air as we pulled up – this was no RTA. What remained of a motor vehicle was smouldering in the middle of the road. There was one male occupant inside the wreckage and a quick appraisal told us he required all the help we could give him. He had blast injuries, resulting in multiple fractures, his right leg was virtually amputated at the knee joint, and his left lower limb was just a fleshy mess. I and David Randall, another paramedic, climbed into the fume-filled wreckage and to our amazement found our patient fully-conscious and able to converse with us.

"Get out! Get out! There might be another one waiting to go off," he kept saying aloud. David managed to cannulate his arm as I set up an infusion pack loaded with Haemacel. A local doctor, who had walked across to the scene, asked if he could be of any assistance.

"Morphine, if you got it doc," I said, and in no time at all, the drug was being administered via the drip feed. I covered, as best I could, the open leg wounds beneath the twisted metal of the dashboard frame and David asked the fire officer if they could remove the car roof, which they did with great zeal. By now, three units of Haemacel fluid had been used, and I was just setting up the fourth, when the medical team from King's College Hospital arrived behind a police escort.

It took another forty minutes to release the victim from the twisted framework and load him aboard *Streatham One India,* for the police-escorted fast run to Camberwell, where surgeons and other hospital staff were waiting for our arrival. Our patient, a Lieutenant General of the Royal Marines, had to have major surgery, which included the full amputation of his right leg. The senseless violence of terrorism had once again bought heartache and tears to to a victim and his family.

It was truly magnificent to work alongside my dedicated colleagues on that terrible day in South London – Tony Seymour, my crewmate for the day, Dave Randall, the other paramedic, Gary Wicks, Chris Green, Mandy Benson and the other emergency team workers who helped make a very difficult job into a life saving operation.

The months rolled by, the long cold winter had at last given way to warmer winds blowing in from the south, the daffodils and cherry blossom pointing the way to the arrival of another spring.

For nineteen months I had been travelling backwards and forwards between the Island and Streatham and I was now getting tired and impatient waiting for a transfer that would base me on home ground. Over the following five weeks at Streatham I decided that if I hadn't heard from the Island service as regards a transfer, I would put in my notice on my next return to the Capital and look for another job on the Island, be it bus driver – postman – railway worker – anything to be with my wife on the Island, leading a normal life. My next few days at home gave me time to draft various job applications, that, if successful, would guarantee us staying in our cottage by the sea.

Back at Streatham early one morning, I received an excited phone call from Jackie back on the Island.

"It's from the railway at Eastleigh, they want you for an interview for a job with the signal engineer's department next week – can you get time off?" she asked.

"Yes I can, I've got some time due to me – I'll get it sorted and ring you back," I said, full of hope.

Four days leave, followed by a long weekend off duty, gave me plenty of time to prepare for the forthcoming interview with the signal engineer at Eastleigh, and with that thought in mind it was a pleasant trip south to the Island, knowing I had nine days at home.

At eleven thirty on the Monday morning of my interview, I walked across the market square of the railway town at Eastleigh to join Jackie at a prearranged restaurant to give her the good news. I had been accepted, and pending the medical I could start with the department in September, just over a month away. We were over the moon.

The medical went well for me and I was advised by a telephone call just as I was preparing for another trip back to London, that my starting date for the position at Eastleigh would be Monday 6th September 1982.

It was a sad day for me as I sat in the watch room at Streatham composing my letter of resignation from the service I loved, the litter bin full of my discarded attempts. With an empty feeling, I stuck down the envelope and placed my future in the station's out-going mail tray.

September 3rd was to be my last turn of duty as a paramedic with the London Ambulance Service, and the four weeks leading up to the final day were to be very busy indeed, putting to test the advanced skills both of Mark, my last crewmate, and myself.

Infusion sets were called for at several road traffic accidents we attended, the worst being a woman trapped under a lorry in the morning rush hour at Tooting Broadway. She was conscious and very brave knowing she was trapped, and despite both her legs being fractured, and blood pouring from head and chest wounds, she assisted us as we struggled under the lorry to carry out as best we could, the infusion, and to seal the wound to the chest. A very brave lady.

Mark and I attended two BBAs in the same afternoon – one at the Woolworth store in Brixton, where mother and baby were being cared for by the shop staff when we arrived – the other in a hotel bedroom at Clapham where the baby a boy was delivered by the father and one of the chambermaids just as we arrived. They were both in a state of shock. Infusion sets were set up on both these BBA calls and, thankfully, both impromptu births were free from any major medical complications.

Sadly, we were called late one evening to another cot-death, at the Tulse Hill Estate near Brixton. Like many others, we were too late to be of any help and another family was left in tears.

My days at Streatham were drawing to a close and in the final week, a surprise party was held for me at the Pollard Oak Public House in Mitcham. It was a memorable evening and a great send off from my working colleagues.

Friday 3rd September arrived, my last turn of duty as a paramedic with the ambulance service. My last call was to an elderly gentlemen, who had fallen downstairs. The removal was a textbook one, reminding me of my training days as a 'greenhorn' all those years ago with the other students at headquarters.

Fifteen hundred hours arrived and I bade my farewells to my friends as I walked out of Streatham for the last time, now a civilian. During my service years I had seen many horrific sights, witnessed rescue operations, seen wonderful togetherness between people, had carried out 78 resuscitation intubations, 56 intravenous infusions, been present at 15 emergency childbirths and attended several major fires in the Capital. But my most important memory was to have had the pleasure of being part of a truly professional workforce – working alongside the men and women of The London Ambulance Service.

PART VI

The Island

It was wonderful to return home to my cottage by the sea and I soon got into the swing of things as I took up my new position working with the signal works department at Eastleigh. I was involved with installing new signalling systems and automatic level crossings at various locations along the south coast. The technical side of the job had changed somewhat since I last worked for the department back in the 1970s and as time went by I was sent on several training courses across the country to update my knowledge as new ideas were put into practice on the rail network.

Two years quickly passed, working for the new works department, when the opportunity arose for me to apply for a signal maintenance engineer's position on the Island. I settled down in the evenings to study, and prepare my self for the forthcoming interview, which went well for me. After an anxious fortnight I was informed that the job was mine. I was to take up my new position on my birthday. What a wonderful present! At long last I had a job on the Island.

For the following fourteen years, along with my colleague Adrian Cooke, we have maintained, traced and rectified signalling faults on the Isle-of Wight railway. A section of electrified railway, eight and a half miles long, with a mixture of old style mechanical signalling alongside a state of the art computerised signalling safety system. The rolling stock - consists of 1938 ex-London Transport Underground Tube Trains – adapted to run on a conductor third rail track. It is a small, but because of it's location, very busy railway, conveying tourists and Islanders alike from the Pier Head at Ryde through the beautiful countryside across the clifftops of Lake and finishing at the seaside town of Shanklin.

Jackie and I moved house three times on the Island over the years, finishing up at a beautiful two bedroomed bungalow at Yaverland, a small modern estate a mile outside the seaside town of Sandown. Many a happy hour was spent upgrading the bungalow to our taste and landscaping the large garden with raised flower beds and an attractive water feature which gave us a lot of pleasure late each evening as a variety of birds used it as a meeting point before flying off to roost in the nearby woodland.

It was here at Yaverland on the last day of November 1998 that my wife Jackie called 999 for an ambulance after I had collapsed with chest pains – my turn had come to be the frightened patient and to experience what it was like to be helped and reassured by two green-garbed paramedics, whose professionalism reminded me of my former occupation and inspired me to write this book.

Following my illness and early retirement, Jackie and I moved yet again, this time to a large ground floor flat in Sandown town centre, with a view of the sea from the balcony.

Our daily walks along the seafront or sunning ourselves on the nearby beach, more than compensate for losing the quiet life we left behind at Yaverland. Sandown, being a busy town, has its fair share of emergency vehicles, and even after all these years, a little bit of excitement, and perhaps a pang of jealousy creeps in as I spot the crews racing to their destination aboard their gleaming white life-saver with two-tones blaring and blue lights flashing...

End

Waterloo Road Control Centre – 1970s – where all the incoming 999 calls for the London Ambulance Service were processed.